Reuel Makes a Decision

RICHARD L. SNYDER

Illustrated by Shirley Hirsch

United Church Press

Boston • Philadelphia

Printed in the United States of America

This book is part of the United Church Curriculum, prepared and published by the Division of Christian Education and the Division of Publication of the United Church Board for Homeland Ministries.

CONTENTS

About This Book

IN THIS book you will meet Reuel, an eleven-year-old boy who lives in Bethany in the year A.D. 32. His father, Hadad, is a shepherd. Reuel does many of the same things that boys today do, and some things that are quite different.

You will also meet Benjamin, Reuel's uncle. He has been one of Jesus' followers, not one of the twelve like Peter, James, or John, but one who traveled with Jesus around Galilee and then to Jerusalem. Benjamin tells Reuel and many other people in Bethany about his experiences.

Both Reuel and Benjamin are storybook people. But Reuel thinks and acts in ways that are true to the lives of boys of his day. Among Jesus' followers there quite likely were men like Benjamin who, after the resurrection, told the stories of Jesus that eventually came to be written down in the Gospels of Matthew, Mark, Luke, and John.

As you read this book you may want to compare Benjamin's stories with the ones in the Bible. To do this, look up the references that are given at the end of the chapters.

CHAPTER 1

News of Benjamin

MORE travelers, thought Reuel, as he noticed a cloud of dust floating above the road that came up from Jericho. Travelers were frequent in Bethany. They arrived just before sundown and, after a night's rest in Bethany, they went on to Jerusalem.

Reuel's eyes followed the dust and the vague figures of the men who were making it, and then he went back to his game of pitching pebbles into shallow holes scooped out of the dirt beside his house. He had been playing with his friend Jonathan, and today Reuel had won two games out of three. But Reuel had bragged about his victories, and Jonathan had gone off angry. It wasn't much fun to pitch pebbles alone.

"Peace, my son. Where will I find Hadad, the son of Joseph?" Reuel made a wild toss as he heard an unfamiliar voice behind him, but he remembered to stand up straight and greet the large man who stood a few feet away. From the dust on the man's robe and feet, Reuel knew he must have been one of the figures he had seen in the distance. The traveler was asking for Reuel's father, who was enjoying the cool shade behind the house, after three days of tending sheep out on the hills.

Reuel took the stranger to his father. He wanted to stay and listen to the conversation, but he knew he should not. Instead he went on around the corner of the house and began piling sticks of firewood into the baskets that he would later carry into the house. In this way he could hear snatches of what the stranger was saying. The name "Benjamin" came clearly to his ears. His uncle! Was he coming home? Reuel heard more of the conversation, "Jesus Christ . . . Damascus . . . he asked me to tell you that he is well and will return soon." The boy wanted to rush up to the stranger and ask questions. But knowing that his father would forbid such behavior, Reuel finished with the firewood, thinking all the time of what it would be like to have Benjamin home again.

Reuel looked at his uncle's empty house next door. He thought about how he used to sit near Benjamin in the pottery shop, watching him turn and shape the jars on the potter's wheel. Once his uncle had let him try to turn the wheel himself, but he soon discovered that it was hard to make the wheel revolve slowly and steadily. He used to spend many hours in the shop asking questions and listening to his uncle tell stories about the places he had seen and the people he had met.

Finally Reuel heard his father say to the stranger, "Go in peace, friend." As the man set off to join the rest of the group traveling toward Jerusalem, Reuel followed his father into the house, where his mother was preparing the evening meal. "Benjamin is coming!" Hadad announced. "He expects to start the journey to Bethany soon. He's going to stay and open up his shop again."

The news so pleased Reuel and his parents that they talked of nothing else all evening. That night as Reuel lay on his mat, wide awake, his thoughts went back to the last time he had talked with Benjamin, and every detail of the strange story his uncle had told came to mind.

On that day there was no school at the synagogue, because it was the day after Pentecost. On Pentecost Reuel's family had eaten the first loaves of bread made from the new wheat and had thanked God for the harvest. Benjamin had missed the feast because he was in Jerusalem. In fact, for months very few jars had been made on the potter's wheel because Benjamin was spending all his time with a strange teacher who had finally been put to death as a criminal.

But on the day after Pentecost Benjamin came back to Bethany. He arrived early in the morning and pushed through the doorway of his brother's house, calling, "Hadad, Hadad, have you heard what happened in the city? Before Hadad could answer, Benjamin began to tell him.

"Early yesterday morning those of us who follow Jesus and believe in his resurrection went to Solomon's porch at the temple. There we spoke to the people and told them stories of Jesus. After a while we all went over to the house where Peter and the other disciples were staying."

Reuel remembered noticing that his father gave Benjamin one of his dark looks. The two men had talked about Jesus before, and they had always parted with Hadad saying, "I will have nothing to do with Jesus." And Benjamin would say, "But he is the one whom God has sent to us."

Benjamin kept right on with his story. "We knew that the men who had been closest to Jesus were eating the harvest bread by themselves in an upstairs room, so we waited below. Suddenly they came running down the stairs to the rest of us. They were all speaking at once, saying, 'Jesus Christ is Lord! God's spirit is among us!' They spoke in such loud voices that many who were in the courtyard heard the shouts and spread the news to others. Soon a large crowd gathered, and many shouted to one another and to Peter. Standing with the other disciples, Peter began to preach to the people. He told them that Jesus who was crucified is Lord and Christ. Many believed Peter and were baptized."

As Reuel lay on his mat picturing in his mind that morning's events, he could clearly remember his father's face. He could almost see him shaking his head sadly as if to say, "This can't be right. My brother has been tricked. He's wasting his time in Jerusalem."

From that day on Benjamin had spent most of his time in Jerusalem with the disciples, and Reuel had seen him only when he returned to Bethany for brief visits. Then one night he had come in a great hurry to tell his brother that he was leaving to go far north to Damascus. The authorities in Jerusalem were putting the followers of Jesus in prison, and it seemed best to leave the city.

That was many months ago and Reuel had not seen his uncle since. But now he was coming home! Reuel wondered what it would be like to have him back. Would he have long conversations with Benjamin in the pottery shop the way he used to? Did his uncle still believe so strongly in Jesus? Would there be trouble between Benjamin and Reuel's father over their different beliefs? These questions tumbled around in Reuel's head until he was overtaken by drowsiness.

Acts 2:1–6, 12–15, 22–24

CHAPTER 2

A Bad Day That Ends Well

ONE morning, several weeks after the traveler had brought news that Benjamin was returning to Bethany, Reuel was outdoors with his friends, Jonathan and Nathanael. The boys were busy setting a snare to catch a large snake when Reuel's mother called to him.

"Your father forgot to get oil from the market. You'll have to get some if our lamps are to burn this evening."

Reuel did not mind having his play interrupted because he liked to go to the market. Soon he was on his way, carrying a jug for the oil and a copper penny.

Just before he reached Bethany's little marketplace, he stepped to the side of the road to let a long train of camels pass. He wondered what they carried in the large bundles strapped to their backs. Were there knives from Damascus perhaps? Or silver bowls from Persia, to be sold in the shops in Jerusalem?

In the marketplace the seller of oil skillfully tipped his large jar so that the oil ran into Reuel's jug. Then Reuel gave him the copper penny and started home.

Just before he came to the hill that led down to his house, Reuel saw Saul, a boy he knew from the synagogue school. Saul was the same age as Reuel but he stood almost a head taller, and he often bragged about his size.

"Hello, little one!" Saul called out to Reuel.

Reuel walked on, pretending to pay no attention. But Saul walked right up to him and repeated his taunt. Reuel could hold his temper no longer. He swung the jug of oil at Saul, but he missed, and the jug fell crashing to the road.

"Too bad, little one!" Saul laughed as he ran off. Reuel stared angrily at the broken jug and at the little pool of oil seeping into the dusty road. Finally he kicked the pieces of pottery into the ditch and shuffled off. What would his mother do? he wondered. There would be no lamps after sunset tonight!

Reuel slipped into the house, sat down by the door, and stared at the floor. "Where's the oil?" his mother asked. "I'll fill the lamps right now."

Reuel answered without looking up, "I broke the jug and lost the oil. But it wasn't my fault. Saul made me mad. He called me 'little one'!"

Reuel still did not look up, but he felt the steady, hard gaze of his mother as she said, "So you got mad at Saul for calling you a name! Is that so terrible, son? Now I'm angry with you! For your carelessness, you can spend the day breaking up firewood and doing other chores."

During the long, long day Reuel worked around the house doing whatever his mother asked. His thoughts went to Nathanael and Jonathan, who were outdoors playing, and then to Saul and what had happened. He knew it had been a mistake to swing that old jug at Saul. But why couldn't his mother understand how he hated to be called "little one"? Down underneath he knew that swinging the jug at Saul had been a foolish thing to do, and although he couldn't quite admit it, he knew that he was more angry with himself than he was with either Saul or his mother.

Finally, the dreary day of chores came to an end. The shadows began to stretch across the dooryard as the sun slanted through the fig trees. Reuel was just breaking up the last few pieces of firewood when the shadow of a man crept across the wood basket and stopped. He looked up and let out a shout. "Benjamin! Mother, come out! Benjamin is here!" he called toward the house, and then he ran to his uncle's outstretched arms.

Some time later Reuel came out of his house, ducked under the fig tree, and called over to his uncle that supper was almost ready. Reuel's father had come home just a little while before and had gone to Benjamin's house to greet him. He had asked Benjamin to join his family for supper to celebrate his homecoming.

It was good to be together like this, Reuel thought as they ate. He felt good for another reason—his mother seemed to have forgotten the broken oil jug and had borrowed some oil from a neighbor so that there could be a lighted lamp when darkness came. Perhaps she had not even told his father!

As they ate Benjamin was eager to hear about all that had happened during his long absence. Reuel told his uncle about what he had been doing at school and about the times he went with his father to help with the sheep.

"You are not far from manhood, Reuel," Benjamin said. "You have grown in many ways."

Pleased and a little embarrassed at these words, Reuel responded only with a smile. His father spoke for him. "Before many weeks have passed Reuel will be twelve. Then just one more year and he will be a man of Israel."

When the meal was finished everyone looked at Benjamin. He seemed to know that they were waiting to hear about his adventures in Damascus.

Benjamin said, "You may be surprised, but I came to like Damascus almost as much as Bethany. There was a time about two months ago when I thought of sending you word that I would not return to my village. The land is so green in Damascus, the waters so fresh, that it seemed foolish to come back again to live where there are more rocks than blades of grass. I had everything I wanted up there. I could work each day, enjoy the city, and meet with the followers of Jesus.

"Many were glad to hear us tell about Jesus. When one of us spoke in the synagogue the people listened eagerly. We told them of Jesus' acts of healing the sick. We told them how he had been crucified and how he had risen and is among us still. To everyone who would listen we told the good news that the messiah has come—that Jesus Christ is Lord. Many hundreds of Damascus people were baptized and became followers. On the first day of the week groups met in homes to break bread together and to offer prayers.

"Then one night, as I sat on the roof of a friend's house and thought of Bethany down here under the moon, I remembered how few of my friends here were Christ's people and realized I belonged in my own village. Of all places, Bethany should know Jesus. So here I am back with my friends and family."

Reuel felt uncomfortable. It was wonderful to have his uncle home, but his talk about Jesus did not seem right. Reuel could see that his father was troubled. Would he argue with Benjamin? At one point Hadad looked as if he were about to say something, but then he stopped. "This is Benjamin's first night at home," Reuel thought. "Father doesn't want to start an argument right off."

Benjamin stood up, stretched, and said, "So, I'm home. I shall begin to make pottery again. There must be many people who need jars and pots. I hear, Reuel, that you need a new jug for oil. Come down to the shop and help me tomorrow."

Reuel looked sheepishly at Benjamin and then at his father. Both of them were smiling. His mother had told them! He had not wanted them to know, but he was glad his father wasn't angry. "All right, I'll be over," he said to his uncle.

The next day after school, Reuel went to the pottery shop to help get it ready for use. He could think of little else but the words that kept humming in his head—"Benjamin will be home for a long time."

He found Benjamin hard at work sweeping and cleaning. Reuel helped him brush the dust from the tables and shelves. Then he watched as his uncle washed and prepared the first batch of clay to shape into jars for the houses in Bethany.

That day there was little talk between Benjamin and Reuel because so much work had to be done. But Reuel felt good just to be in the shop again, and he knew his uncle liked having him around. There would be many hours of good talk and stories, Reuel knew, just as there used to be.

CHAPTER 3

Has the Promised One Come?

IN THE days that followed, Reuel worked at the pottery shop whenever he could. Benjamin was busy making jars and talking with the many people who stopped by to greet him. Everyone seemed glad to have Benjamin back—or so Reuel thought until one day at the synagogue school.

The rabbi began with prayers as usual. Then he took the scroll of the prophet Isaiah and set it on the reading desk. But before anyone could read his portion, the teacher began to talk about Isaiah and what he had written.

He said, "This writing tells of the hope we have for the days to come. Isaiah tells of a mighty leader whom God will send. Have you heard these words before?

"For to us a child is born,
  to us a son is given;
and the government will be upon his shoulder,
  and his name will be called
'Wonderful Counselor, Mighty God,
  Everlasting Father, Prince of Peace.'
Of the increase of his government and of peace
  there will be no end,
upon the throne of David, and over his kingdom,
  to establish it, and to uphold it
with justice and righteousness. . . .

"We still look for this leader. He will come. But some foolish men in our village and in other places say that he has already come. But I ask you, does their Jesus sit upon the throne of David? No! He died on a cross, the way a criminal dies."

Reuel was certain that the boys were looking at him as the rabbi spoke. They all knew about his uncle. If only Benjamin had not come back to Bethany! If only he'd forget his teaching about Jesus! But these thoughts were quickly pushed aside as Reuel realized that he could not let Benjamin go undefended. Summoning all his courage, he asked for permission to speak. When the teacher told him to go ahead, Reuel said, "My uncle, Benjamin, is a follower of Jesus. He says that Jesus did many good things when he lived. Jesse, the grandfather of David here, tells everybody that Jesus healed his leg." David nodded in agreement with what Reuel was saying.

"Do *you* believe that Jesus is the one promised to our people by the prophets?" the teacher asked Reuel.

Reuel could feel the eyes of every boy in the class on him. "No, Rabbi, I do not." He spoke with great assurance.

The rabbi nodded in approval and went on with the lesson. But Reuel's mind stayed on Benjamin. He wished he had not said that "No, I do not" quite so firmly. He felt as if he had been a traitor to his uncle. Yet he had spoken the truth. He did not believe that Jesus was the promised one.

Reuel was afraid his friends would tease him about his uncle. But when the class was dismissed, all the boys except David hurried off as if they were avoiding him. David and Reuel started down the road together. "Reuel," David began, "it makes no difference to me what the rabbi says. I know that Jesus healed my grandfather. No one else could do that."

Reuel did not know what to say, so he talked of other things until they separated at the path that led down to David's house.

Ordinarily Reuel stopped at the pottery shop on his way home from the synagogue school, but today he went right to his own house and sat down under the fig tree to think.

Benjamin had said many times that Jesus was the promised one. David had said that Jesus did marvelous things. But his own father and the rabbi thought that Jesus was no different from other men and that the promised one was still to come. Surely the rabbi and his father could not be mistaken. For that matter, how could his uncle really believe that a man who had been crucified as a criminal could possibly be the leader for whom the Jewish people had been waiting?

By the next day the subject of Benjamin and the other followers of Jesus had been forgotten by the boys. At least they made no mention of it and included Reuel in their games and talk as usual. But the questions were still going around and around in Reuel's mind. He decided he would stop in his uncle's shop today and ask him why he was so sure Jesus was the promised one.

He found Benjamin kneading the clay for the next day's work. The boy stood at the door for a few minutes trying to think what to say. When his uncle greeted him, he responded politely. Then he picked up a piece of clay, rolled it into a ball and tossed it into the air over and over again. Finally he threw it into the corner with the trash. Benjamin smiled a little as he watched. He knew Reuel was thinking about something.

Reuel sat down on the low bench near the door and, without looking at Benjamin, said, "I want to know something. Why do you think Jesus is the promised one?"

Now Benjamin knew what was bothering Reuel. He walked over to his nephew and sat down beside him.

"Perhaps you remember that I was away from Bethany many times when you were younger," he began. "You know that I was traveling with Jesus up in Galilee. I saw Jesus help people who were sick. One day he healed a blind man. I heard him speak kind words to men who could not go to the synagogue because they failed to keep the laws. I was a follower of Jesus because I believed he was a very great teacher, perhaps a prophet. But until he was put to death I was not sure what he meant to me. You have heard this, Reuel?"

"Yes, but how did Jesus' death make a difference to you? You cannot follow someone who is dead. Besides, many people say that Jesus was a criminal."

"Yes, that is what they say. And he was crucified because the authorities believed he was a dangerous man. But you have heard me say that Jesus Christ lives. This I believe, Reuel."

Reuel did not know what to ask next. He had not learned anything new or convincing from what his uncle had said, but he wanted him to go on.

Benjamin sensed this and said, "I'll tell you how I came to believe this. Two followers of Jesus—Simon, a friend of mine, and a man named Cleopas—told me a story that helped me. They said that they were walking out to Emmaus, a village on the other side of Jerusalem, on the first day of the week after Jesus had been crucified. They were going home. All their hopes that Jesus was to be a great leader were dead. There was nothing for them to do but go back to Emmaus. 'People may laugh at us at first,' they said, 'but in a few months they will forget that we followed a failure.'

"So the two men made their way along. Once, just before the road dipped sharply, Simon looked back at Jerusalem and sadly shook his head as he recalled all that had happened during the last few days—Jesus was dead; no more could he believe that a leader had come to bring a new day of glory to the Jews.

"The two men were so deep in their own thoughts and conversation that they were not aware of other travelers on the road. But, suddenly, they say, a stranger joined them and asked, 'What were you talking about as you walked?'

" 'We have been talking about Jesus of Nazareth, a mighty prophet,' Cleopas answered. 'Surely you have heard about him. How could you have come from Jerusalem and not know what has happened there?'

"The strange traveler did not answer, but his expression said that he wanted to hear more. So Cleopas continued. 'Well, the religious and the Roman authorities wanted to get him out of the way, so they put him to death on a cross. Here it is the third day after his death, and we who were his followers are going home.'

"When they reached Emmaus, Simon and Cleopas started to leave the road. They realized that the stranger intended to go on with his journey, but since it was late they stopped him and asked him to spend the night with them. This he agreed to do.

"As they sat at supper in Cleopas' house, the stranger gave thanks for God's goodness, then picked up the bread, broke it, and passed it around the table. Suddenly they knew! This man was no stranger! This was Jesus!"

Benjamin paused, as if he had reached the end of his story.

"What happened then?" Reuel asked. "Did Jesus stay with them?"

"They said that Jesus left them as quickly as he had come," Benjamin answered. "Then the two said a hasty good-by to their families and set right out on the road back to Jerusalem.

"When they reached the city they went directly to the room where Peter had been staying, hoping to find him. To their surprise they found not only Peter, but also many of the other disciples. Without asking the reason for the meeting in the middle of the night, Cleopas and Simon breathlessly told all that had happened on the road. Then they reported how, in the breaking of bread, they knew that Jesus was with them.

"But you know, Reuel," Benjamin said, "they were not the only ones with news. They found that Peter had met Jesus too. He had called the disciples together and with great excitement had told them 'Jesus lives! I know he lives! I have met him!'

"I follow a living Lord, Reuel, and I know that I must always be his disciple. That's why I must tell the good news about Jesus to everyone who will listen!"

Isaiah 9 : 6–7 ; Luke 24 : 13–35

CHAPTER 4

A Trip to Bethphage and a Story

FOR a number of days Reuel spent most of his spare time helping his father with the sheep, which were grazing not far outside Bethany. He thought about Benjamin's strange story and almost asked his father about it, but decided against this. Perhaps when he talked with his uncle some more he would understand the story better.

One evening Benjamin came over to Reuel's house and said, "Tomorrow I'm going to take my pots and jars to sell in Bethphage. How would you like to go with me? You can lead the donkey while I keep a hand on the load as we go up and down the hills."

"I'll go, I'll go!" Reuel replied quickly. "I'll ask Father."

Hadad gave his permission, and early the next morning, before hardly a rooster had crowed, Reuel and Benjamin began to load the donkey. Reuel carried the jars out to Benjamin, who was careful to pack them securely, placing straw mats between them so that they would not crack or break with the jolting and bumping along the road.

The journey to Bethphage took almost two hours. It was midmorning when Benjamin arrived at the marketplace to show his wares. Business was good. Reuel guessed that people had broken many jars while his uncle was in Damascus and they were eager to buy new ones.

When the sun was high, Reuel and Benjamin found a place a little distance from the marketplace where they could sit in the shade and eat the lunch they had brought with them. They had talked very little during the morning because customers had kept them busy. But now that the donkey was browsing in the thin grass behind them and Benjamin was not trying to interest a householder in a new water jar, there was time for conversation.

As uncles often do, Benjamin put a question to Reuel about school. "What scrolls are you reading these days, Reuel?"

"The prophets," Reuel answered. "We've just started to read in the book of Jeremiah."

"Does the teacher say much about the meaning of the Scriptures?"

Reuel paused. He remembered what the rabbi had said about Jesus and wondered what he should tell his uncle. "Just lately he has been saying more," Reuel answered. "He speaks often of the leader we expect God to send to us. Once he mentioned Jesus, but he said that Jesus could not be the one."

Benjamin made no response. Surprised that his uncle did not explain why the rabbi was wrong, Reuel said nothing more. The only sound was that of flies buzzing about their heads until they began to hear the voices of people gathering in the marketplace again.

As they got up to go, Benjamin said, "Reuel, perhaps your teacher is alarmed because some of the men of Bethany are listening to my teaching. I've promised to meet them at sundown today in the courtyard of my house. Perhaps you will want to listen too."

Reuel did not answer because he wasn't sure what he should do. His uncle did not press him for a reply.

When the last jar had been sold Reuel and his uncle set out for the long walk home. As they trudged the hot, dusty road in silence, Reuel thought about the gathering that night at Benjamin's. Should he go? Should he tell his father about it?

At supper that evening, Reuel told about the trip, but he said nothing about Benjamin's plans for the evening. Reuel had by this time made his own plans, and these did not include asking his father's permission.

After Reuel had eaten he stood in the yard for a while, watching the swallows make circles in the evening sky. Soon he heard footsteps in front of the house. He tried to keep himself out of sight as he looked out to the road and saw the fathers of several of his schoolmates coming to Benjamin's house.

Then, when no one was looking, he quickly climbed up into the fig tree where he could look down into Benjamin's yard and hear what was being said. He found a good, sturdy, lower branch and made himself comfortable while he waited for Benjamin to begin. He felt quite pleased with his plan. He wasn't really trying to hide, he told himself, and he was here in the tree just because he was curious about who would come to hear his uncle.

He listened to the conversation among the men. Some of them asked about Jesus, and Benjamin answered their questions. Then Benjamin said, "You are not the only ones who ask about Jesus. In many villages and cities men are telling about his life and answering questions as I am trying to do. I will tell you all I know about him.

"Jesus began to be known around Galilee soon after his friend, John the Baptist, was arrested by Herod. Jesus was about thirty years old, a carpenter from Nazareth. Wherever he went he told the good news of the kingdom of God, saying, 'The day promised by the prophets of old is right before us. Turn to God and believe this good news.'

"I first heard of Jesus while I was visiting in Capernaum. A friend, Thaddaeus, told me about him. He said that he had been listening to

Jesus and that I should go to hear the words of truth that Jesus was speaking. During my stay in Capernaum, I did as Thaddaeus suggested.

"By this time Jesus had gathered a little band of followers. Four fishermen—Peter, Andrew, James, and John—went with him everywhere. Others, like my friend Thaddaeus, followed along, trying to learn all they could from what Jesus said.

"One sabbath, Jesus and his followers went into the synagogue and joined the faithful in reading the Scriptures and listening to the scribes tell about the law. During the service Jesus read a passage and then stood in front of the congregation explaining it. All of us were astonished at his teaching. Someone said, 'This man says new things. He does not repeat the teaching of the scribes. He speaks on his own authority.'

"Soon the wondering murmurs of the people were cut off by a shout from a back corner of the synagogue. We all turned around and saw a wild-looking man with dirty clothes and a scraggly beard, crying out like one possessed by an evil spirit, saying, 'Why are you here? Have you come to destroy us? I know who you are; God has sent you.'

"Jesus spoke in a quiet voice. He told the evil spirit to be silent and to come out of the man. Suddenly the spirit was gone and the man was free and well.

"All around the synagogue we could hear people saying to one another, 'What is this? Who can this man be, that evil spirits listen to him and do what he says?'

"As the men left the synagogue and went home, the news about Jesus' new words and power spread all over the city. That day and into the evening a great many people came to him for help and to listen to his teaching.

"The next morning, just at sunrise, Peter awakened Thaddaeus to tell him that Jesus had been up for several hours and had gone off by himself. We did not want to be left behind, so we hastily got up, threw our robes around us, and went out. We found Jesus just outside the city. When we saw that he was praying, we stood a short way off. After a while Peter said to him, 'People in Capernaum are looking for you, even this early in the morning. What shall we tell them?'

"Jesus did not answer right away, and we could tell that he was thinking about what he should do that day. Then he said, 'Let us go to the villages near here. We cannot help only the people in Capernaum. I want to preach in other places too.'

"That was the beginning of one of our journeys through the villages and countryside of Galilee."

As soon as Benjamin finished the men began to ask questions. Reuel wanted to sit in the tree and listen, but the first stars were shining brightly, and he knew that he must go in the house. So he stretched his cramped legs and hopped down from the tree. Neither his mother nor father asked him any questions about what he had been doing. His plan had been a good one. Perhaps he would try it again.

Mark 1:14–15, 21–28, 35–39

CHAPTER 5

Another Story Heard in the Fig Tree

WHEN he was not helping his father with the sheep, Reuel spent a great deal of time in the pottery shop with his uncle. Sometimes they talked, but often Benjamin was busy at his potter's wheel, carefully shaping the jars and bowls with his fingers as he worked the wheel with his foot. By watching his uncle and by trying to work the wheel himself Reuel discovered that making pottery takes concentration and skill. One day after trying several times, he made a small lamp which Benjamin said was almost perfectly shaped. Reuel took it home and proudly showed it to his mother.

Reuel noticed that David's father was the most frequent visitor among the many people who stopped by the shop. It was from their conversation that Reuel found out when the men were next meeting at Benjamin's house to hear about Jesus. Reuel wondered why his uncle had not told him. Did he see him in the tree last time and guess that he had not asked permission? Or did his uncle not see him and think that he wasn't interested or that his father had forbidden him? As he thought about it, Reuel decided he was better off not knowing the answers to these questions. This way there was nothing to prevent him from doing the same thing again. He often climbed the fig tree, and there was no harm in listening to Benjamin's teaching since Reuel knew that he did not believe in Jesus even though he liked to hear about him.

That evening as the men began to gather at Benjamin's, Reuel climbed into the tree and found a comfortable spot where he could sit and swing his legs and listen to Benjamin.

"As I traveled around the Galilean countryside with Jesus and his followers," his uncle began, "I learned about some of the things Jesus had done in Capernaum before I met him. I'll tell you about some of them and also about some things I saw myself.

"As the followers of Jesus went about Capernaum, visiting with friends and buying grain and oil in the market, word spread that Jesus was living in the city. Very quickly townspeople came in droves to his house. They were everywhere, packed into the room where Jesus sat and clustered about the doorway, trying to hear him preach the good news of the kingdom of God.

"When it seemed that there was no chance for another person to find standing room, there was a noise on the roof, and before the people could discover the reason, clay and twigs began to rain down on them. Then the saplings that held the roof together were pushed aside. Next a mattress was let down through the hole, with slings made of ropes fastened to the ends. On it was a man who could not walk because his legs were paralyzed.

"Four men peered down through the opening in the roof and asked Jesus to help their friend. The faith of the four was so great that Jesus could not deny their request. Jesus looked at the man and said, 'My son, your sins are forgiven.' To everyone's amazement the man stood up, rolled up his bed, and pushed his way to the door. The people praised God and said, 'We never saw anything like this.'

"Many times Jesus helped the sick. One sabbath when he went to the synagogue in Capernaum, he saw a man sitting near the door. The man's hand was twisted and held against his side, useless for any way of earning a living. Looking across the synagogue, Jesus saw some Pharisees watching him. He guessed that they were waiting to see whether he would help this man on the sabbath. If he did, then they would accuse him of breaking the sabbath laws.

"Jesus called the man with the useless hand to him. Then he turned to the row of suspicious watchers and said, 'Is it lawful on the sabbath to do good or to do harm, to save life or to kill?' But not one of the men gave an answer. Perhaps they were afraid to risk a disagreement with

this man who did mighty things for people wherever he went. Then as all the sabbath worshipers watched, Jesus turned to the crippled man and said, 'Stretch out your hand.' The man did so, and his hand seemed to become well. He lifted it high, as if to offer praise to God.

"After this the men who had been watching so carefully went out and looked for others who were already worried about this man named Jesus. Together they tried to find ways to put a stop to his work.

"Jesus was always reaching out to those who needed help, or to the underdog, or to people whom others ignored or thought were unimportant. One day that I remember, some mothers brought children to Jesus so that he might bless them. The disciples tried to stop them. After all, Jesus was a busy person, and there were many who needed help. Jesus saw what was happening and became indignant. 'Let the children come to me,' he said. 'Do not keep them away. You of all people should know that the kingdom belongs to those who are like these children. Mark this as true: only those who are as trusting as children shall be part of the kingdom of God.'

"The disciples felt ashamed and let the children come close to Jesus. They should have known that Jesus would welcome the children. Yet, I, too, would probably have held them back had I been among those closest to Jesus, trying to protect him from the crowds. We watched as Jesus gathered the children around. He talked to them and took some of them in his arms and blessed them."

Reuel was so engrossed in the last story that he did not notice how dark it was getting. He quickly slipped out of the tree and into the house.

"You've played outdoors late tonight," his mother said. "I was beginning to think your father would have to go out looking for you."

"I'm sorry. It got dark so quickly," Reuel explained as he hastily unrolled his mat and prepared to go to bed. Relieved that there were no more questions, he closed his eyes and drifted off to sleep thinking about the stories Benjamin had told.

Mark 2:1–12; Matthew 12:9–14; Mark 10:13–16

CHAPTER 6

Sheep and Shepherds

AS REUEL and the shepherd, Nathan, strode into Bethany, spirals of smoke were beginning to rise from the cooking fires, showing that supper was being prepared in the homes of the village. Reuel walked with steps that seemed bigger than those that only two days before had carried him around the village—perhaps because he was having a hard time keeping up with Nathan, but also because he felt like a man. For the first time he had been a real shepherd—not just a helper, but a shepherd. Reuel's father and the other shepherds were taking their sheep some distance from Bethany for grazing, and just before they were to leave, one of the men had become ill, so Reuel had gone in his place and stayed out with the sheep overnight. Now he was returning with Nathan, whose turn it was to come home.

All day yesterday while his father led the flock, Reuel looked after the strays, keeping them away from thorn bushes, or ravines, or other dangers. He noticed that his father always seemed to know what was happening to the sheep and where the possible dangers lay. In the evening as the shepherds sat around the fire, Hadad told about the night just a few weeks before when he had killed a wolf that had almost taken a lamb. Reuel wondered how his father could do such a brave thing.

But most on Reuel's mind as he walked into Bethany were his father's words to him as he sent him home with Nathan: "You're a good shepherd, Reuel. You've shown me that I can count on you to work hard and put the welfare of the sheep above everything."

Reuel left Nathan and hurried toward the pottery shop to tell his uncle about his two days as a shepherd. Even though it sounded a little like bragging, he repeated what his father had said.

"That's a very fine compliment." Benjamin smiled at Reuel as he spoke.

A little embarrassed now, Reuel hastily began to talk about his father and the other shepherds and the care they took of the sheep. Benjamin listened closely, and when Reuel was finished he said, "Jesus told a story once that suggested that shepherds are a little bit like God himself."

This idea startled Reuel. "What was the story?" he asked.

"Jesus asked if a shepherd who had a hundred sheep and lost one would not always leave the ninety-nine and look for the one that was lost. When the lost one was found, the shepherd would go to his neighbors and friends and invite them to rejoice with him. Jesus went on to say that God rejoices over every sinner who returns to him, much as the shepherd rejoices over the sheep he has found."

"I like that story," Reuel said. "Jesus knew what shepherds are like. My father would go after a lost sheep just as the shepherd in the story did, I know. He'd even risk his own life to save a sheep."

"I guess when Jesus told that story about the shepherd he was thinking that people are a lot like sheep," Benjamin commented.

"What do you mean by that?"

"Well, I mean that we all get lost and do a lot of wrong things, the way sheep do if they don't have a leader. And because Jesus saw that people were like this he helped them. He went around to all the villages preaching and healing."

Benjamin's words reminded Reuel of something he had wanted to ask. "If Jesus was so good and helped people so much, why was he crucified like a criminal?"

"That's a hard question," Benjamin answered. "I'd have to tell you the whole story of Jesus' life to answer it. But you began to get a little idea of why people got angry with Jesus from some of the stories I was telling the other night when you were up in the tree."

So his uncle knew he was there all the time! Reuel tried to hide his surprise by going right on with the conversation. "You mean the Pharisees who thought it was wrong to help people on the sabbath and things like that?"

"Yes. And then there was another kind of thing Jesus did that made some people angry. He was willing to eat and be friendly with sinners and even tax collectors. For instance, very often at the end of a day Jesus and his followers met in his house in Capernaum. The door was open to all who would come, and many did. Among the regular visitors were some men who collected tolls just outside Capernaum. On this particular day these toll collectors brought with them three other men of the city who had been told to stay out of the synagogue because they had failed to observe the laws about food and fasting.

"Jesus asked a few of the men to prepare some food so that all who were present could have their supper together. As the bread was broken and passed from one to another, the men told about how they were called sinners. They said that their families were taunted and treated as outcasts because they did not obey all the religious laws or because they collected taxes for the Roman government.

"Jesus listened with interest to what the men were saying. Those who were in the room hoped he would have something to say, as he had on other occasions. But before he had a chance, a voice came from outside the house: 'Why does he eat with toll collectors and sinners?' Jesus looked up to see several scribes of the Pharisees gathered at the open door. The one who had asked the question was speaking to the disciples, but he was looking right at Jesus.

"Jesus came toward the doorway and spoke to the scribes: 'Those who are well have no need of a physician, but those who are sick do need one. I have come not to call the righteous, but sinners.' Without saying another word, the scribes turned and went on their way.

"Another time Jesus was entering Jericho. Some friend must have spread word of his coming, for crowds lined the road. Jesus had rounded a turn in the road when the rest of us came up to see a strange sight. There, sitting on the lower branches of a wild fig tree was a man dressed in costly robes. So wealthy a man is not often found sitting in a tree!

"We saw Jesus look up at the man and speak to him. The words were a surprise even to us—'Zacchaeus, hurry and come down. I must stay at your house today.'

"It was clear as Zacchaeus started down that he was not used to climbing in and out of trees. We heard from those in the crowd that he was one of the head collectors of tolls from the traders and merchants coming into Jericho. As we looked at him we could understand why he had climbed the tree. He was very short and probably could not see over the crowd. He walked over to Jesus, bowed a greeting, and led Jesus to his house.

"We ate in Zacchaeus' dooryard. After Jesus and his host had finished the meal, they came out under the trees. Zacchaeus said that he had often taken more than he should from the traveling merchants. Then he said, 'Look, I will give half of all I have to the poor, and if I have cheated anyone I will give back four times as much as I have taken.'

"When Jesus left Zacchaeus, he said to all who were standing in the courtyard, 'Today salvation has come to this house, since Zacchaeus also is a Jew, a son of Abraham. You know that the Son of man came to seek and to save the lost.' The people who had gathered around were perplexed, and some of them were angry. 'The great teacher has been in the house of a man who is a sinner,' they said."

Reuel puzzled over this story as he left the shop to go home for his supper. This wasn't as easy to understand as the one about the shepherd and the sheep. Reuel remembered the time a traveler had come to his house and asked for a drink of water. The man was well dressed and had a kind face. Reuel's father gave him a drink and some dates and bread, but Hadad would not eat with the man. When Reuel asked the reason, his father said it was against the law to eat with a sinner, and it was best to think of strangers as sinners until you knew otherwise. Jesus had eaten with men he *knew* were sinners! It could not be right for a good Jew to do that!

Luke 15 : 3–7 ; Matthew 9 : 35–36 ; Mark 2 : 15–17 ; Luke 19 : 1–10

CHAPTER 7

Questions About the Sabbath

BECAUSE no work could be done on the sabbath, Reuel always had extra chores on Friday. This meant he had to leave his uncle's pottery shop early to get home in time to do them. As he hurried along the road he met Laban, a boy who lived a short distance from Reuel's house. The two boys had never been good friends, even though they lived quite close to each other.

Reuel explained to Laban that he was hurrying because his father would be coming in from the hills just before sundown. Then the sabbath observance would begin.

"I'm lucky," Laban said. "I don't have to do any chores. And besides, tomorrow I'm going to Jerusalem to visit my cousins. We're going to watch the contests the Roman soldiers have in Jerusalem."

Reuel had heard before about the Roman foot races and games of skill. "I think it's foolish for grown-up men to have contests and races. They're for boys," he said. "And besides, a good Jew wouldn't watch the Romans! Especially on the sabbath!"

Laban responded angrily, "You can't fool me. You wish you could go with me, but your father won't let you!"

Reuel started to give an angry answer, but instead he walked off, leaving Laban standing in the road.

That evening Reuel told his father about the conversation.

"Yes," Hadad said, "there are many Jews who are not faithful to the law. But in this family we will be faithful always. We do no work and no traveling. We will do nothing that the law forbids."

"But you would help someone who needed help on the sabbath, wouldn't you, Father?" Reuel asked. "Benjamin says that Jesus healed people on the sabbath." The words were no sooner out than Reuel realized he should not have mentioned Jesus.

Hadad's face clouded. "That depends, my son. Some of our teachers say that certain acts of mercy are allowed, but other rabbis are very strict. We will not follow the ways of Benjamin's Jesus in any case."

Reuel quickly nodded in agreement, hoping to end the discussion, but his father went on. "Reuel, have you been going to your uncle's to hear his teaching? One of the shepherds said he saw you there last time, and I remember that you were very late coming home that night."

"I wasn't really there," Reuel stammered. "That is, I wasn't *over* there. I mean, I wasn't in Benjamin's courtyard."

"Well, where were you?" Hadad was impatient now, and Reuel knew that only the truth would do for an answer.

"I was in the fig tree. I just climbed up to see who would come to hear Benjamin. I listened to the stories, but I don't believe as Benjamin does. I don't believe in his Jesus."

"I'm glad to hear that," Hadad said. "But you are to stay away from these meetings. You are not to listen to my brother's teaching. Do you understand?"

Reuel meekly nodded his head.

On the day after the sabbath, Laban had more to say about his trip to Jerusalem as the boys gathered outside the synagogue before school. Reuel ignored him, but he found himself thinking again about the question he had asked his father. What Laban and his family did was wrong. There was no doubt about that. But what about the things Jesus did on the sabbath? And how could you tell what was right or wrong if you ever started breaking the sabbath rules the least bit?

Reuel was glad his father had said only, "You are not to listen to my brother's teaching." Just talking to Benjamin was different from listening to his teaching, Reuel decided. After all, his father and Benjamin frequently talked together, and Reuel knew they talked about Jesus sometimes. "So," Reuel said to himself, "there's no reason why I shouldn't go and ask Benjamin some questions."

His uncle was talking with some men when Reuel entered the shop, so he busied himself with rearranging some of the jars on the shelves. When the men were gone Benjamin turned to Reuel and asked, "What's on your mind?"

Reuel told his uncle about Laban. "I know that what his family does is wrong," Reuel said, "but you think that what Jesus did was right, and he broke the sabbath law too."

"Yes," Benjamin replied. "Jesus and his followers did break the sabbath law, or at least they went against the strict rules of the scribes and Pharisees. But Jesus always had a good reason. For example, one sabbath after Jesus and his followers had been to the synagogue, they decided to go out from Capernaum. As they walked they came to some grain fields, golden brown in the sunlight, with the full heads of grain bent over from their own weight. The disciples were very hungry, so Peter took some grain, rubbed it between his fingers to take off the husks, and ate the kernels. The other disciples did the same thing.

"Some Pharisees who were nearby noticed what the disciples were doing and came up to Jesus. 'Why do you let your followers do what the sabbath law forbids them to do?' they asked angrily. 'Have you forgotten what the scribes tell us? Surely you know that on the sabbath it is wrong to pluck grain.'

"Jesus turned to them and said quietly, 'The sabbath was made for man, not man for the sabbath.' "

"But does that mean it's all right for Laban to stay away from the synagogue and go into the city to watch the Roman games?" Reuel asked.

"I don't think so," Benjamin said. "Remember this: Jesus had been to the synagogue that sabbath. And even though the disciples were not going very far, they were hungry. So Jesus said that man's need came before strict keeping of the law, because the sabbath law was made for man's benefit. I, too, have a hard time saying just what laws we must keep or just how we are to interpret each law, but Jesus' words seem right to me."

"But Laban could say that going to the games instead of to the synagogue is *almost* the same as plucking grain," Reuel said, more to prove to himself that he could argue with Benjamin than to make a point.

"I don't think so," Benjamin answered. "Jesus went to the synagogue faithfully, and he did not break any of the important laws—the laws of Moses. But he did not follow all the strict rules and the interpretations of the law that the scribes and Pharisees have made. For example, the rule about washing before eating did not seem important to Jesus. One day in Capernaum many people gathered to listen to him. Several of us noticed that there were unfamiliar faces in the crowd. Thaddaeus found out that the men were scribes from Jerusalem. Of all Jews, these men were famous for their teaching about the law. They would have all of us be as strict as they are. We wondered if the local Pharisees, out of their own devotion to the religious laws, had asked the scribes to come up.

Perhaps the scribes could prove that Jesus was wrong in what he was saying and doing.

"When it was time for the noon meal, we all took our lunches, that is, all but the scribes and the Pharisees who were busy watching the rest of us. We could see them glare as some of the disciples began to eat without washing their hands. Moving closer to Jesus, the scribes and Pharisees asked, 'Why don't your disciples live by the teaching of the scribes? Don't you know that they are eating with unclean hands?'

"Jesus said to them, 'You have a fine way of letting your own traditions get in the way of God's commandments.'

"Then Jesus called the people to him and said, 'Hear me, all of you, and understand: there is nothing outside a man which by going into him can make him unclean; but the things which come out of a man are what make him unclean.'

"As we walked back to Capernaum that day, we talked among ourselves. One disciple said, 'I didn't want to wash before eating, once I knew those scribes from Jerusalem were spying on us.' Another said, 'Yes, and think of the shepherds and farmers and others; how can they follow the rules those men teach? The words of Jesus make sense to me—that it is what comes from the heart that is most important. The evil comes from there, not from our failure to do what the scribes tell us.'

"What Jesus was determined to say to the scribes and Pharisees," Benjamin concluded, "was that the righteousness God requires is more than following strict rules; it is truly loving God and man."

Once again Reuel left his uncle without knowing what to believe. Certainly what Jesus said seemed to be right. But then, the scribes had been helping the people to understand the law for a long time. They had authority too.

Mark 2:23–27; Mark 7:1–16

CHAPTER 8

Sons and Fathers

ONE warm afternoon instead of going to the pottery shop, Reuel took the small lamp he had made some time ago and set out with his friend Jonathan to explore a cave in the side of a hill not far beyond the olive trees. The boys had been there before, but they could not go very far into the cave because it was very dark and they had no lamp with them. But this morning at school they had made plans to go again, this time equipped with Reuel's lamp. Jonathan brought along oil and the kindling set from his house.

The boys talked about what they might find in the cave. Had robbers been there? Had they left anything behind? Jonathan even asked, "Do you think there might be animals—a fox maybe?"

When they reached the cave they crouched just inside the opening and struck the flint and iron together. Finally the sparks caught on a few dry leaves, and from the fire they lighted the lamp. Reuel went first,

carrying the lamp, and Jonathan followed. Some bats were hanging above, but the boys were not afraid of them.

Reuel moved cautiously as he led the way farther back into the darkness. Suddenly Jonathan, who was on Reuel's heels, stumbled and fell forward, throwing Reuel against the wall. The lamp fell and broke into a hundred pieces. "You clumsy fool," Reuel scolded as soon as he caught his breath. "Now we can't see anything!"

"I couldn't help it," Jonathan said, "I stumbled."

Neither boy would have admitted it, but they were a little afraid there in the blackness of the cave. Without too much trouble, however, they felt their way back. A few steps around a large rock brought them to where they could see daylight streaming into the cave's entrance.

On the way home the boys argued. Reuel said Jonathan was clumsy and blamed him for spoiling their plans and breaking his lamp. This made Jonathan so angry that he walked off and left Reuel to go home by himself.

But Reuel decided not to go home. Instead he went to the pottery shop. Benjamin glanced at him as he came inside. He guessed that his nephew was troubled about something, but he did not ask any questions. After a few minutes of puttering around, Reuel said, "Sometime I need to make another lamp."

"Oh," Benjamin responded, "what happened to the one you made before?"

When Reuel finished explaining Benjamin asked, "And how do you feel about it all now?"

"I guess I'm not really mad at Jonathan anymore. I guess he probably tripped on a rock that he couldn't see in the dark. Besides, now I'd like to go back some day and really explore that cave. But I don't think I can tell Jonathan that."

"You mean that it's pretty hard to let Jonathan know you're sorry?" Benjamin asked.

"Yes, and something else too. If I ask him to come with me, maybe he'll still be mad and won't come."

"I suppose that's possible, Reuel, but you can't tell. He may be ready to forgive you for what happened."

Reuel thought about that idea for awhile.

Benjamin finally broke the silence. "Have I told you about the time Jesus talked about forgiveness?" he asked.

Reuel shook his head, and sat cross-legged on the floor as Benjamin began his story.

"One day many people were gathered around Jesus—Pharisees, sinners, and ordinary folk like us. Jesus taught them as he often did by telling a story. This one was about a prosperous farmer who had many fields and a large number of cattle. His two sons, both grown men, worked with him. Together they bought and sold animals and directed the work of the laborers in the fields.

"The younger of the sons became bored with this life. He dreamed for many months of going to one of the cities he had heard about from travelers. He thought that if he lived in such a place he could do as he pleased.

"After thinking about it for a long time, he went to his father and asked, 'May I have my share of the property?' Being the younger son, he expected to receive one day a third of everything that belonged to his father.

"The father realized that his sons might like to have their shares before he died. So he divided all that he had between them. Before many days had gone by, the younger son took the money, and what property he could carry on some donkeys, and set off for a city far from home.

"He found what he was looking for—good times and friends with whom to share his good times. He lived recklessly, spending his money without thought for what would happen when it was gone. He also forgot to follow the ways of life that his father had taught him.

"After a time, food became scarce in the city where he was living. Few people had enough to eat. With his share of his father's property sold and the money spent, he was hungry and homeless. His friends deserted him. There was nothing to do but become the servant of a landowner. He was given the job of feeding the pigs that were penned in the man's fields. Even the animals' food seemed good to him, he was so hungry.

"In time the son realized how foolish he had been. He thought of home and knew that his father's servants were better fed than he was. More and more often he wondered about returning to his father. He even thought about what he would say when he stood before him. Perhaps he would begin, 'Father, I have sinned against God and I have done wrong. Take me in as one of your laborers.' Would his father be kind to him, in spite of his foolish behavior? he wondered.

"When he could no longer stand his life as a keeper of pigs, he set out for home. As he was coming down the last stretch of road, he looked ahead and saw his father running across the fields toward him. The father put his arms around the young man and greeted him with a kiss.

"The son remembered all that he had planned to say. 'Father, I have sinned against God, and I have wronged you. After all that has happened, I have no right to be treated as your son.'

"But the father, full of gladness at the young man's return, said to his servants, 'Bring quickly the best robe and put it on my son, and place a ring on his finger and shoes on his feet. Take the calf that is being fattened and kill it. We shall have a feast and be joyful.'

"When everything was ready, the father looked again at his son and said so that all might hear, 'This is my son who was counted as dead. He is alive again! He was lost and gone from me, but now he is found!' "

Reuel had listened attentively. This was a strange story. He had never heard one like it from the teacher at the synagogue school. Certainly the son had no right to be welcomed back by his father. But the father had forgiven him!

"There's more to the story," Benjamin explained. "But it's late now. Come back tomorrow and I'll tell you the rest."

Luke 15: 11–24

CHAPTER 9

Benjamin Tells More About Sons and Fathers

THE next day at the synagogue school the boys sat in their places facing the rabbi. The teacher always stood when he read from the Scriptures, and so did each of the boys when it was his turn. Jonathan had been reading from the prophet Jeremiah and was just sitting down when his eyes met Reuel's. No word had been spoken between the two since the adventure in the cave. But as they looked at each other for a moment, it seemed to Reuel that Jonathan smiled at him. He couldn't be certain.

When school was dismissed an hour later, Jonathan started for home without waiting for anyone. Reuel caught up with him and walked along beside him for a few moments without saying a word. Then, taking hold of Jonathan's sleeve, Reuel said, "I'd like to explore that cave again. Can you meet me there this afternoon?" Jonathan looked surprised at first. Then he nodded his head, slapped Reuel on the back, and ran off toward his house.

As soon as Reuel had eaten lunch, he went to his uncle's shop and examined the lamps on the shelf. Benjamin looked up from his wheel. "That would be a good lamp for exploring a cave," he said, as Reuel picked up a small one. "You may have it," Benjamin added.

Reuel was surprised that his uncle seemed to know exactly what he was thinking. He thanked him, took the lamp, and hurried off.

Hours later, when he returned from the cave, Reuel stopped at the shop to return the lamp, now sooty at the tip where the light had been burning. He said, "The lamp is still good, Benjamin. Thank you for letting us use it. That cave isn't so big after all. We walked for about fifty paces and then came to a wall. That was as far as it went. There were some bats around, and there were a few old bones on the floor. Nothing very exciting, but we had a good time. Jonathan's a real friend!"

Benjamin smiled.

"I'm ready for the rest of the story, if you have time now," Reuel said. "You stopped yesterday with the father having a big feast for the son who came back home. I thought that was the end of it."

Benjamin started immediately.

"I didn't mention yesterday that while Jesus was telling about the father's great joy, the Pharisees began shaking their heads. They couldn't understand why a father should treat a son in such a way—a son who could only be called a sinner.

"Jesus went right on with the story. He said that the older son had been in the fields and did not know that his brother had returned until he came near the houses and heard music and the sound of dancing. As soon as he reached his own house he called to one of the servants and asked, 'What does all this mean? Are there guests at my father's house?'

"The servant told his master, 'Your brother has come home. When he was still coming down the road, your father ran out to meet him. The fatted calf has been killed and is now being roasted. Your father is overcome with joy because your brother is back. None of us ever expected to see him again! That's the reason for the celebration.'

"But the older brother did not share in the joy at his brother's return.

Angrily he strode into his own house instead of joining in the merriment at his father's.

"When the father heard that his older son had returned from the fields, he went to him and pleaded with him to join the festivities. But the son said, 'For many years I have been faithful to you. I have served you in the fields and in your house. I have done whatever you asked me to do. And what have you done for me? Not once have you ever given me a kid so that I could have a feast with my friends. But now this other son of yours comes home, penniless, hungry, and dirty, having wasted everything you gave him, and you kill the fatted calf for him! What do I care for him and for your celebration?'

" 'But you are always with me,' the father responded. 'We have shared everything. All that is mine has been yours to use in any way you please. When my other son came home, I was filled with joy. It seemed right to celebrate. Your brother was the same as dead. Now he is alive and with us. He was lost and now he is found.'

"When Jesus finished the parable, the crowd was silent, except for the scribes and Pharisees who talked angrily among themselves. They probably thought Jesus was saying that they were like that older brother, and I think perhaps he was. But I think he was saying something about the father in the story, too—something about the love a good father has for his son. And I think he was saying that God's love is like this."

Reuel sat thinking for a while. It had been a good story, one of the best his uncle had told, but it was puzzling too. He couldn't help wondering if the older brother wasn't right in resenting the feast for his younger brother. But then Reuel liked the father in the story, too.

"I think my father would be like the father in the story." Reuel sounded a little surprised at his own thought. "But I'm not sure he'd like the story," he added.

Benjamin looked intently at Reuel. "I believe you are right," he said thoughtfully.

Luke 15 : 25–32

CHAPTER 10

The Way of a Neighbor

ONE afternoon Reuel and Jonathan went out on the hillside behind Bethany. For a while they threw pebbles at a snake that was sunning itself on the rocks. Then they waded through the stream, enjoying the coolness of the water on their feet.

As they started to return to Bethany by the road that the travelers took to Jericho, they saw two figures that looked like Roman soldiers walking along, kicking up a cloud of dust. All the children in Bethany knew a Roman soldier when they saw one, even though not many passed through their village. But whenever Reuel made a trip to Jerusalem he saw many of them. Some, dressed in colorful uniforms, stood guard at the outer gates of the temple.

The men coming down the road were not so colorfully dressed, but as they came closer, there was no doubt that they were soldiers. Jonathan tugged at Reuel's sleeve, pulling him back in the direction from which they had just come. Reuel had the same idea. Quickly they ran down the slope and stayed out of sight until the soldiers were far down the road. Would the men have forced them to carry their packs? they wondered. The boys had never been ordered to carry a soldier's pack, but now that they were older this could happen to them.

That same evening Benjamin ate supper at Reuel's house. Reuel told about seeing the Roman soldiers that afternoon.

"Twice I have had to carry a soldier's pack," Benjamin said. "One of the times, the last, up near Capernaum, I offered to carry it another mile."

Reuel was used to hearing his uncle say strange things, but this was too much! Hadad stared at his brother in amazement. "You offered to carry the load another mile!" he exclaimed. "You must have been out of your mind!"

"Perhaps I was," Benjamin responded. "But I did it because I thought the soldier might discover I did not hate him. This is something that Jesus asked his followers to do. Like you, when I first heard the teaching I thought it was foolish. Why should I try to help a Roman soldier? But after I tried it I decided that it was far better than just doing my duty and then cursing the soldier afterwards, as I had always done before."

"But the Romans are our enemies," Reuel's father protested. "They rule over us, and they do not worship the Lord God. We don't want them in our land."

Benjamin spoke again. "Yes, we do feel that way. But perhaps God would rather have us love our enemies. I'll tell you what Jesus told us when a scribe asked him a question like this."

Reuel watched his father closely as Benjamin hesitated for a moment before beginning his story. Reuel had been feeling a little guilty about listening to Benjamin's stories in the pottery shop. Now he was seeing his father in the same situation. Would Hadad say that he didn't want to hear any more about Jesus? Benjamin started to speak. Hadad kept his eyes on the floor and said nothing.

"One day when Jesus was teaching in Judea, not far from Samaria, a scribe stood up to ask him a question," Benjamin began. "The scribe said to Jesus, 'What shall I do to inherit eternal life?' No one made a sound as we waited to see what Jesus would say. Certainly not one of us had ever heard a more important question.

"Jesus replied, 'What is written in the book of the law?'

"The scribe answered, 'You shall love the Lord your God with all your heart, and with all your soul, and with all your strength; and your neighbor as yourself.'

"Jesus nodded and said, 'You have answered correctly. Do this and you will live.'

"Of course, we all nodded. We had heard the law about loving God and neighbor for as long as we could remember. What answer could have been better?

"Then the scribe asked Jesus another question: 'I know the Scriptures tell me to love my neighbor, but who is my neighbor?'

"Jesus answered by telling a story. He said a man was making his way down the steep and rocky road from Jerusalem to Jericho, and as happens to many who make that trip, he was attacked by robbers. They took away his clothing and all his possessions, beat him, and ran off, leaving him close to death. A priest who was off duty was going down the same road. When he came upon the man lying there, he crossed to the other side and kept right on going. And then a Levite came down the road and saw the man, but he too crossed to the other side and continued on his journey.

"But a Samaritan came to the spot where the man was lying, and he went over to him and treated his wounds. Then he put the injured man on his donkey and took him to an inn. The next morning the Samaritan gave the innkeeper enough money to care for the man for several days. 'If you need to spend more than this,' he said, 'I'll repay you when I come back this way.'

"Then Jesus looked at the scribe and said, 'Which of these three men acted as a neighbor to the man who was robbed?' Of course, the scribe could only answer, 'The one who showed mercy on him.'

"And Jesus said to the scribe, 'Go and live in the same way.' "

Reuel knew his father was bothered by the story, but he did not seem angry with Benjamin for telling it. "Is this not a new teaching?" Hadad asked.

Benjamin replied, "Yes, and we were amazed at it. Here we were, not far from Samaria, all of us hating the Samaritans because they do not keep the religious law as we do. And yet Jesus made the neighbor in the story a Samaritan, not a priest or a Levite, or even one of us good, though ordinary, Jews."

Reuel's father was quiet for a long time. Finally he said, "I do not like this teaching."

Benjamin looked at his brother kindly. "I know Jesus' teachings are hard to accept. For a long time I questioned them myself. But do not close your mind to them, my brother."

Hadad did not respond, except to say good night to Benjamin as he left. Reuel got out his mat and went to bed, wondering what thoughts lay behind the troubled look on his father's face.

Matthew 5:41; Luke 10:25–37

CHAPTER 11

An Adventure on the Caravan Road

ONE warm day Reuel and Jonathan sat in the dooryard of Jonathan's house trying to think of something to do.

"I know," Jonathan said. "Let's go down and watch for caravans."

Reuel thought that was a fine idea, so the two boys set off for the Jerusalem road. Both Jonathan and Reuel had been forbidden to go near the caravans, because their parents thought the strange-looking camel drivers might be dangerous. But this was not the first time the boys had disobeyed.

Soon a caravan came along, and the boys watched it go by. Then Reuel had another idea. If they climbed a low, rocky hill, they could look down on the road and throw pebbles at the camels.

"The pebbles won't hurt them," Reuel said, mostly to reassure himself, "and it will be fun to see what happens."

Jonathan needed no persuading, and by the time the next caravan came into sight both boys were ready with pebbles in their hands. When the animals were directly below them, they let fly. The pebbles struck one camel so directly that it stumbled and almost fell. The man walking at its head grabbed the lead rope and quieted the animal. Another man turned in the direction of the boys and shouted and shook his fist at them. Reuel and Jonathan did not wait to see what the men would do next. They ran down the hill and out of sight as fast as they could.

Reuel told no one about the episode. Making the camel drivers angry did not bother him. He rather enjoyed remembering the one who had shouted at them. But the memory of the camel that almost fell down haunted Reuel for a long time.

Some days later Reuel had another chance to help his father out on the hills. He worked hard, and he could tell that his father was pleased with the way he handled the sheep.

When he and his father had a chance to rest and talk, Reuel brought up a question that had been on his mind. "If I took a knife from the ledge near the well, if it wasn't mine but nobody said it was his, would that be wrong?"

Reuel had seen the knife one morning on the way to school, but he had not picked it up, much as he wanted it. He had been pleased with himself, because he knew he had done the right thing. What was really on his mind now was not so much the knife as a question he had been thinking about ever since he had thrown the pebbles at the camels.

Hadad replied much as Reuel thought he would. "Would you want God to know you took that knife?"

"Do you mean that God always watches me?" Reuel was sure that was what his father meant, but he asked anyway.

"Not exactly, son. I mean that there's nothing we can do that doesn't make a difference to God and to someone else. God wants us to treat others in the same way we would like them to treat us. This is what my rabbi taught me when I was your age. I've tried to live by it."

"And if we don't, does God punish us?" This was the question Reuel really wanted to ask.

"I believe so, Reuel. Many of the great prophets of our people have spoken about God's punishing our wrongdoing."

"But they've said that God will forgive people, too, haven't they?" Reuel asked.

"Yes, some have spoken of this." Hadad seemed lost in thought now, so Reuel wandered off to see if the sheep were all right. His own thoughts were all in a jumble. Would God punish him for what he did to the camel? Or was God like the father Jesus told about?

Several days later Reuel talked with his uncle about these things. He told Benjamin what he and Jonathan had done to the camels. He told him about the conversation with his father, also. "What do *you* think?" he asked finally.

"You've asked a difficult question," Benjamin answered. "There is no simple answer. I believe that God is a loving father who cares for us all. I believe he is like that father who ran out to meet his son. Once I know that, I seem to be better able to care for others and to want to do what is good. I don't know about God's punishment, but I know that we feel pretty miserable when we've done wrong. I know, too, that God expects us to do what is right and good."

"But sometimes it's so hard," Reuel said. "And sometimes you don't mean to do anything bad, but you do anyway."

"I know," Benjamin said. "I guess we all know. But because we make wrong decisions or don't think about what we're doing, bad things happen; people are hurt—and camels, too." Benjamin smiled at Reuel, but the boy did not notice because he was staring at the floor.

Suddenly he looked up. "Wouldn't it be something if everybody did what God wanted—if people shared things and treated everybody right, and didn't do anything that was unfair or that hurt people!"

"It certainly would be," Benjamin agreed. "You know, Reuel, it's too bad you never heard Jesus."

"Why?"

"Because he said something that was a little like what you're saying now. He was talking about the way things will be in God's kingdom, when people truly love God and live as he wants them to live. He said, 'Blessed are you who are poor in earthly goods, for the kingdom of God belongs to you. Blessed are you who know hunger now, for you shall be satisfied in the kingdom of God. Blessed are you who weep now, for in the kingdom of God you will laugh. Blessed are you who are hated now, who are kept out of the synagogue, and are called evil because of the Son of man! In the days to come you will rejoice and leap for joy. Consider this—your reward is great in the life that is coming. Your fathers in Israel treated the prophets shamefully, too.' "

"Do you think things will ever really be this way?" Reuel asked.

"In God's kingdom, yes," Benjamin replied. "And Jesus said that God's kingdom could be in our hearts even now, if we would live in the new way."

"What's that?" Reuel asked.

"The way we've been talking about, and the way Jesus himself lived. It's different from the teachings of the religious leaders in the synagogues. They say, 'This is the law. This you must do to please God.' But Jesus reminded us that God doesn't just give us a set of rules that tell us how to live. He taught us a new way of love, he lived in this new way himself, and he showed us that God alone can help us, by his love, to do the right thing."

Luke 6:20–23

CHAPTER 12

Reuel Learns More About the New Way

ONE day when Benjamin had to go to Jerusalem, he asked Reuel to stay at the shop in case anyone came to buy jars and bowls. A few customers came, but not enough to keep Reuel busy. He was amusing himself by tossing pebbles at a line he had drawn in the dust when Ruth, an old lady who lived at the edge of the village, shuffled up to the doorway and called for Benjamin.

"Benjamin isn't here," Reuel explained. "He's in the city. He asked me to help anyone who wanted to buy pottery."

"I have broken my milk jar," Ruth said. Reuel noticed how bent over she was. He knew that she was so old she could no longer straighten up.

Reuel hurried into the shop and came back with a large jar which he held out to the woman. She shook her head. "That's much too big. There are only three of us at home, and anyway the goat is too old to give that much milk. Get me another."

Reuel quickly looked over the jars on the shelves and returned with a smaller one. Ruth nodded and asked the price. The boy remembered what Benjamin had told him about the prices of the different size jars. "One denarius," he said.

The woman stepped back. "I don't have anything but a few copper coins. Aren't they enough?"

Reuel was not supposed to bargain with the buyers. He felt sorry for the woman, but he could not disobey Benjamin. Politely he told her that he could not sell the jar for less than one denarius. She shook her head and started to walk slowly away. Just then Reuel saw his uncle coming down the road. "Wait, Ruth," he called, and at the same time he waved to his uncle to hurry.

Benjamin greeted the woman and asked what she wanted. When she told him, he took the jar from Reuel's hands and gave it to her, accepting the pennies that she held out to him. Both he and Reuel bid her peace and health as she turned to go home.

Benjamin said, "You were following instructions in refusing to sell the jar to her, Reuel, but I know Ruth, the mother of Saul. She has little money to spend on jars. I took her pennies because that was what she was able to pay."

Reuel was glad that Ruth had her jar, but he wondered if it was fair to charge only about half the price. He thought of other people in Bethany. None were wealthy. Laban's father owned many fields, but most of the people had barely enough flocks and fields to live on. When crops were poor even Reuel's family did not always have enough grain. Sometimes they had to sell a sheep or two to buy flour, which they tried to stretch as far as possible. Reuel got only one new robe each year. Sometimes in the night he would hear his father and mother talking about how hard it was to find the money for taxes or for a synagogue offering.

"Ruth is very poor," Reuel agreed. "But the rest of us don't have much either."

"That is true," said Benjamin, "but it is no reason for failing to help one another."

Reuel had another thought. "I remember what you told me Jesus said about the kingdom belonging to those who are poor in earthly goods. Does this mean that the people who serve Jesus will someday become rich men with all they want to eat?"

"It hasn't been happening that way," Benjamin answered. "Certainly I'm not rich. Perhaps Jesus meant that when God finally rules in men's lives, they will have all they need. I'm not sure about that, but I *am* sure that God cares for everyone. And I'm sure that we who love him belong to his kingdom and must show his love to others.

"One time when Jesus was talking about the new way of life, he said, 'If you show love to those who show love to you, what difference does that make in God's sight? Even the toll collectors and the sinners love those who love them. If you do some good thing for those who have done something good for you, what credit is it to you? Everybody does that much. If you greet your own people and say "peace" to them, what are you doing that others do not also do? Even the gentiles do that, and they do not even pretend to worship the Father in heaven.'

"Then Jesus spoke to us of what God expects of us in the kingdom. He said, 'You are to love those who are opposed to you. You are to do good to all men, and lend to those who have need, expecting nothing in return. Then your reward will be great, for you will be living as sons of the God who rules over all men. You will be showing God's goodness in your lives—God's goodness even to the ungrateful and to the selfish.' Then Jesus summed up all that he had been saying, 'You must be perfect as your heavenly Father is perfect. In your life with others, be merciful, even as God is merciful.' "

Reuel thought of what he had seen his uncle do for the old woman who had come for the jar and of all that Benjamin had told him about Jesus. He knew that the new way of the kingdom of God was not an easy one. But it sounded right to him in a way he could not explain.

Luke 6: 32–36; Matthew 5: 46–48

CHAPTER 13

Almost a Man

ONE morning Reuel and his father arose very early and went to Jerusalem where Hadad was to deliver some sheep. After this was done, the boy was given permission to go wherever he wished.

Jerusalem was a puzzle to him; he knew the hills and valleys outside the city much better. He could see the temple standing high above all the other buildings, and he started to walk toward it. But he never reached it.

Inside a courtyard he saw a small crowd listening to a man, and he stopped to see what was happening. Reuel could not hear all that the man was saying, but he did hear one of the bystanders ask a question, addressing the speaker as "rabbi." As Reuel moved up close he could tell that the teacher was discussing the law. The rabbi spoke for some time, and even though Reuel could not understand everything, there was something about the man that drew the boy to him. Finally, when the sun was high, the rabbi gave a sign. The people stood, bowed their heads, and turned and left the courtyard. Reuel left, too, hurrying to the gate where he was to meet his father.

The homeward journey was pleasant. With the sun beginning to cast long shadows, Reuel could make himself appear to be as tall as his father if he walked in just the right place. Tiring of this game after a while, Reuel began to tell his father about the rabbi he had heard. "Why do those men spend their time just listening to him?" he asked.

Reuel's father thought a bit and then said, "I think that the man must be a teacher with great knowledge about the law. The men want to know how they should live so as to be in favor with God." That was all he said. By this time they were climbing the Mount of Olives and it took all their breath to go up the steep slope.

As he climbed Reuel was thinking. "I wonder," he said to himself, "if Jesus was a little like that rabbi. Maybe there was something about him that made people want to listen to him and follow him even if they didn't understand why they wanted to. I'll have to ask Benjamin about that sometime."

When they reached the top Hadad and his son sat down a little way from the road to rest. This time Hadad started the conversation.

"Reuel," he said, "your speaking of that rabbi reminds me of something I've been thinking about. Your twelfth birthday isn't far away, and then in just another year you'll be a man of Israel. It pleases me that you were interested in that teacher and in what he was saying, because this shows that you are almost a man."

Reuel listened eagerly as his father went on.

"But what I've had on my mind for some time is this: you've been very good helping with the sheep lately, and I've decided that you are almost ready to take charge of the flock part of the time. So, beginning with your twelfth birthday, you are to spend as much time as you can with the sheep. When they must be taken some distance away for grazing, you will go along, even though you may have to miss some school."

No news could have pleased Reuel more, or made him feel more grown up and ready to do a man's work.

"This means you won't have so much time to play with the other boys," Hadad added.

"I don't care. The games aren't as much fun as they used to be. Most of the boys are younger than I am. Besides, I'd rather be doing a man's work than playing with the boys," Reuel said with a good deal of pride in his voice.

Hadad smiled at his son. "I may even be able to increase the size of the flock with you as regular shepherd. Then we could earn more money."

"We can have a bigger flock," Reuel said. "I'll work hard."

"I'm sure of that." Hadad got up and led the way down to the road.

CHAPTER 14

Benjamin Asks Reuel a Question

THE next day as soon as school was out and Reuel had had something to eat, he went to talk with Benjamin. He started right off with the news that he would be a full-fledged shepherd beginning with his twelfth birthday. He and Benjamin talked for a long time about what this would mean—the nights out on the hills sleeping in the open, cooking on open fires, going after sheep that strayed, perhaps even having to kill the wolves that sometimes attacked the sheep.

"It will be a hard life," Benjamin said, "but I know your father finds it a good one, and I think you will too."

Reuel nodded in agreement. "Maybe some day we'll have a hundred sheep in our flock. Maybe then we can have a bigger house and a yard with a dozen olive trees, as Laban's family does."

"Perhaps," Benjamin agreed a bit skeptically. Then he asked abruptly, "Reuel, what do you really want to do with your life?"

Reuel puzzled over what his uncle meant. Finally he said, "Of course, I want to be a man of Israel, a faithful son of the law." Reuel meant what he said, and yet he did not know how to say all that he meant. Partly because he did not know how to answer the question, he turned the conversation back to Benjamin. "How did you come to be a potter—and a kind of teacher too?"

"My father, as you know, was a potter, and I learned from him, whereas your father began when he was very young to go out into the hills with his uncle's sheep, so he quite naturally became a shepherd instead of following his father's trade.

"But more and more as I worked as a potter I found myself looking for something. I would listen to almost any teacher who came along. And when I heard of some new teacher, or someone claiming to be the messiah, I would go to hear him. Most such teachers were in Jerusalem, so I would go there frequently."

"I heard a teacher when I was in Jerusalem last week," Reuel interrupted. He went on to tell his uncle about stopping to listen to the rabbi. "Your Jesus must have been a little like that teacher I saw," he concluded.

"Jesus was the kind of teacher who attracted people. I can't explain why I kept on following him, why I wanted to hear every word. You know, I did not decide that I wanted to be a disciple until after Jesus had been killed, until I found myself joining the disciples in saying that the risen Christ is with us. Then I knew somehow that I *had* to be a follower—that Jesus Christ himself was calling me. During his ministry, though, there was a pull I could not fully understand, but I think it had something to do with the authority with which Jesus spoke. I guess it was also his loving concern for people. Perhaps most of all it was the feeling I had that I was learning from Jesus about our God in a way I had not learned from any of the rabbis to whom I had listened. I suppose it was this same pull that made the disciples say 'yes' when Jesus called them."

"Did they all say 'yes' right away?" Reuel asked.

"The four fishermen did. I guess they had seen Jesus and heard him preach a few times. One day Jesus came along the shore of Galilee as Simon and Andrew were casting their nets. He hailed the two men and said, 'Come, follow me, and I will make you fishers of men.' Simon and Andrew put down their nets right there on the shore and followed Jesus. With James and John it was the same. I don't know about all the other disciples, but I know that Matthew responded right away. He was a toll collector and was at work collecting on the road into Capernaum. Jesus seemed to know Matthew, for he went right up to him and called him by name. Then he said, 'Follow me.' And Matthew got up and left his table."

"And these men were among the twelve special friends of Jesus, weren't they?" Reuel asked.

"Yes, in a way you could say that Jesus had many disciples, but from among the group of followers he chose twelve to be his closest companions. These were Simon, whom Jesus called Peter, and his brother Andrew, James and John, Philip, Bartholomew, Matthew, Thomas, James, the son of Alphaeus, Simon the Zealot, Thaddaeus, and Judas Iscariot. The twelve men were to be with Jesus for a time, and then they were to go out and preach to others. Also, they were to have the power to do many of the mighty acts that Jesus had been doing to help the sick and crippled."

Another question occurred to Reuel. "I wonder how Jesus himself knew what to do—why did he decide to do the things he did?"

"I guess no one can answer that question, but I do know he was certain that God had called him to a special mission. While he was still a carpenter in Nazareth he must have thought many times about the messiah who was to come, about what God was calling our people to do. Maybe he went around listening to various teachers just as many of us do. I know that he went to listen to John, the baptizer, a prophet who preached to all who would listen, telling them to be baptized to show they were sorry for disobeying God. John dressed in the roughest sort of clothing and lived out in the open, eating whatever he could find in the fields.

"Jesus went to hear John preach near the Jordan River. There Jesus was baptized. He became very sure that God was calling him to be his servant. After that Jesus went away into the wilderness and prayed for many days. When he came out of the wilderness he was much more sure of what God wanted him to do."

"Nobody knew then, though, what kind of leader he was going to be, did they?" Reuel asked. "I mean, nobody thought that things would end the way they did and that, later on, people would believe he was the promised one?"

"That's right," Benjamin answered. "I'll tell you about that sometime, but it's time to close up the shop now and go home for supper."

Mark 1:16–20; Matthew 9:9; Mark 3:14–19; Mark 1:4–13

CHAPTER 15

Who Is Jesus?

REUEL and Benjamin were on their way to the pottery shop with a load of clay that they had dug together at a clay pit outside the village. There was little to do except talk because Benjamin's donkey was doing the real work of carrying the clay.

Benjamin took up the question Reuel had asked before. "I think all of us who followed Jesus thought of him at first as another rabbi. Then after we knew him better, we had to make up our minds about what he was doing. We couldn't help but have many questions. After all, we had seen him heal a man with a useless hand; we had heard his sharp words to the scribes of the Pharisees; and we had stood by as he called children to come to him. Also, very often as we came to a new place, villagers would come up to us and ask, 'Who is this Jesus you follow?' At one stopping place, some of the scribes who lived there asked us, 'What has your teacher said about himself?' But none of us answered them. We did not know how. As for myself, as you know, I would not have said that Jesus was the promised one, because I was not convinced of this until much later. Even those closest to Jesus, like Peter, seemed to be unsure."

By this time Reuel and Benjamin had reached the shop, and Benjamin waited until they had unloaded the clay before he said anything more. When they had sat down just outside the shop Benjamin started again.

"Let me tell you a story Peter told some of us not long ago. He said that this happened when Jesus and the twelve went up to a place called Caesarea Philippi, not long before Jesus started the journey to Jerusalem that was to lead to his crucifixion.

"Peter said that as they walked along Jesus suddenly asked the disciples who were with him, 'Who do men say I am?' At first no one answered, and then one by one they spoke up: 'Some people say you are John the Baptist'; 'Elijah the prophet'; 'One of the prophets.'

"Then, according to Peter, Jesus looked directly at the disciples and asked, 'But who do you say that I am?' Peter said he answered, almost without thinking, 'You are the Christ.'

"Jesus responded, 'Tell no one about me!' "

"But why did he say that?" Reuel asked.

"I wish I knew, Reuel," Benjamin answered. "As I said, the story is one that Peter told us, and he did not try to explain it. I think Peter believes now that Jesus thought his purpose was to be the Son of man, the announcer of God's kingdom. But Peter himself admits that, at the time, he could not understand at all when Jesus told the disciples that he was going to suffer many things, that people were going to go against him, that they would probably even kill him. This wasn't Peter's, or anybody else's, idea of a messiah. Peter said that he couldn't believe this would happen to Jesus and he told him so, but Jesus rebuked him. At that time no one could understand that the promised one would need to suffer."

Reuel had been listening closely to what his uncle said, but he could not understand about Jesus as the promised one. As he got up to go home, he said to Benjamin, "I still don't understand what Jesus was trying to do. It doesn't make sense to me."

Benjamin smiled. "It is hard to understand. Even I do not fully understand. Keep asking questions, Reuel. Keep on trying to know the truth. That is what I did as I followed Jesus and then joined the company of his disciples."

Mark 8:27–33

CHAPTER 16

To Benjamin's—Together!

FOR several days Reuel did not have a chance to talk with Benjamin, but he kept thinking about some of the things his uncle had said. Then one evening Reuel saw the men beginning to gather at Benjamin's house. If only he could join them, he thought. Maybe he would understand more if he could hear the questions the men asked as well as what Benjamin said. As Reuel stood at the door he suddenly heard his father's voice speaking to him. "So Benjamin is going to tell more of his stories tonight. You have heard quite a few of them in the pottery shop, haven't you?"

Reuel swallowed hard. Was his father going to forbid all talks with Benjamin?

Hadad continued, "I'm not angry with him or with you. I know how it is—Benjamin is so full of his stories that you find yourself talking with him about Jesus even if you don't mean to. But I would like to know one thing: Why do his stories interest you?"

Reuel did not know what to say. Why was his father asking this question? "I—I don't know," Reuel stammered. "His stories are good. And I just like to listen to him, I guess."

"You know, Reuel, I haven't made up my mind about Benjamin and his stories. I've talked for many hours with my brother. At first I was sure that he was entirely wrong in his ideas about Jesus, but now I'm less sure."

Reuel could hardly believe his ears.

Hadad continued, "Tonight I'm going over to Benjamin's. I cannot believe that he is right about Jesus being the promised one, but I want to hear his stories." Then he paused and turned to Reuel. "You may come, too, if you wish."

There was no hesitation in Reuel's response. "I want to go! The last of the men are coming now. Let's hurry!"

Reuel and Hadad hurried over to Benjamin's dooryard. This evening Reuel sat right in the middle of the group of men, beside his father.

"I was telling last time about an argument the disciples had," Benjamin began. "One day as Jesus and his followers were walking down the road, some of the twelve began discussing who was the first among the disciples, and who would rule with Jesus when he became known among the people as the messiah.

"Jesus must have guessed what was on their minds, because that evening he asked, 'What were you discussing on the road today?' When no one answered him, Jesus sat down with the twelve and said, 'If any one of you expects to be first in the kingdom of God, he must be willing to be last. He must live as servant of anyone who needs him.'

"As if to show what he meant by the puzzling words, Jesus got up and went over to a doorway where a little child was standing. He brought him over and set him in the middle of the group. The child looked strange among the men. Jesus looked at the bewildered faces of the disciples and then took the child in his arms again, saying, 'Anyone who accepts such a child in my name is really accepting me. And know this, if you accept me, you will know God's presence, not mine only.'

"After that, the twelve and the rest of Jesus' followers talked less about their own greatness. Jesus' example in taking the child in his arms made us all less sure of our own ideas. But, even so, I guess we still didn't fully understand about being servants.

"We were traveling again several weeks later. Jesus, the twelve disciples, and a few of us who had been with Jesus for some time were going south toward Jerusalem. In spite of all Jesus had said, it was hard for us to realize what his work really was. We had seen him heal many people. We had heard him speak in ways that should have told us that he was interested only in doing God's will and serving his fellowmen. And yet, we could not forget our hope that he would be a mighty ruler.

"Sometimes when we traveled, the disciples would try to push their way to the front so that they could walk with Jesus. One day James and John, the sons of Zebedee, did this. As they walked along, one on either side of Jesus, they said, 'Teacher, we want you to do for us whatever we ask you to do.' 'What do you want me to do?' Jesus asked. James and John replied, 'When you rule in kingly power, let us sit on your right and on your left.'

"As Jesus listened to them, we could see a shadow come over his face. He looked as if he were disappointed in his friends. Then he spoke to them, and I think he meant for us all to hear because his voice was strong and full. 'Are you able to share my suffering and my troubles?'

"James and John replied with confidence, 'We are able to do that.' Jesus looked at them sadly. He explained that they would indeed share in his troubles. He could promise them that, but he could not promise them glory or fame for these were not his to give.

"As the rest of us overheard this conversation, we became disturbed at the selfishness of James and John in asking such things of Jesus. Looking back on it now, though, I guess we were a little jealous.

"Jesus was aware of our feelings. Perhaps he heard us muttering to one another. So he called us together, and as we clustered around him, he said, 'You know that the rulers of the gentiles think of themselves as proud and mighty, and that those who govern the people often do evil things with their power. That is not the way it will be among you who would belong to the kingdom of God. In that kingdom, greatness belongs to the man who serves others. Are you not able to see that I have come to serve, even if this means that I must suffer and die?'

"As the days went by we remembered what Jesus had said about the opposition he was going to meet from the authorities, and we became somewhat afraid ourselves. I must confess that I wondered if I had done the right thing in following Jesus. We all knew that the work of Jesus was beginning to mean something quite different to us from what we had expected. We wondered more and more what he meant about being a servant."

Because Reuel wanted to stay to hear the questions the men would ask, he hoped his father would not notice how dark it was getting. But just as soon as Benjamin ended his story, Hadad leaned over to his son and told him that it was time he went home. Reluctantly, Reuel obeyed.

As he lay down on his sleeping mat, his head whirled with the excitement of all that had happened that day. What a surprise to be able to go to hear Benjamin's teaching *with* his father! Would they go every time? Would his father come to believe that Benjamin's teaching was right?

Reuel could only guess at the answers to these questions. And he knew he would have to keep on guessing for a while because his father would be off with the sheep early tomorrow and would not be back for several days. But he did know one thing: he was glad that he and his father had gone together to hear Benjamin.

Mark 9:33–37; Mark 10:35–45

CHAPTER 17

A Game, A Quarrel, and a Story

ONLY rarely these days did Reuel have time to play with the boys of the village. But one afternoon they persuaded him to join them in a game of "hide and seek" on the hillside. There were a few low places in the ground and some big boulders that provided good hiding places.

Twice Joseph, who was younger than most of the boys, was it. When, for the third time, he was the first to be found, he got angry. "You fellows aren't fair," he cried. "I bet you looked when I hid!"

Joseph directed this accusation at Laban who had just caught him.

"I didn't look!" Laban protested.

The other boys defended Laban. "He didn't cheat," they agreed.

"You did too cheat! I know you did!" Joseph shouted. He picked up a handful of small stones and threw them at Laban and then turned and ran towards home.

The boys yelled after him, calling him a bad sport and saying that they were glad to see him go. Laban was not hurt, but the argument had spoiled the game. For a while the boys stood around complaining about Joseph's bad temper and childishness. Then Jonathan, who had been quiet up to now, glanced around the circle of boys and said, "I wonder if anyone did cheat and spy on Joseph."

After a long pause Laban spoke up. "I did sort of, I guess. I didn't do it on purpose. I just opened my eyes and there he was, slipping into the hole over there by that flat rock."

Reuel moved from where he had been leaning against the rocks, stood up straight, and spoke slowly and firmly. "Then Joseph was right. The game wasn't fair. Joseph shouldn't go off angry. It was our fault. Come on, let's go to his house and ask him to come back. We can tell him what happened."

"I'm not going," Laban said. "Joseph shouldn't have thrown the pebbles at me. Besides, I didn't mean to cheat."

"Come on," Jonathan said, taking Reuel's side of the argument. "We have to tell Joseph we were wrong."

Slowly, the boys got up and marched down to Joseph's house. They found him sitting behind the stable, looking at the ground. All the boys mumbled a greeting and then stood there without saying anything. Finally Laban spoke up. "We're sorry about the game," he said. "I did cheat, but I didn't really mean to."

Jonathan added, "We won't cheat again—not any of us."

Joseph could hardly believe what he was hearing. He stared at the boys; then he jumped up and said, "Let's go play again. I'll be it!"

The group followed Joseph back up the hill. They played until the sun was low in the sky, and they knew it was time for evening chores.

Reuel walked home with Laban. They didn't say much to each other, but Reuel wasn't as uncomfortable as he often was with him. As Reuel said good-by, he gave Laban a little poke in the ribs and said, "Let's play on the hill again tomorrow."

Laban's eyes brightened. "Sure," he said, "I'll meet you there."

At the same time that Reuel reached his house, his father came in from the hills. Reuel greeted him with a question. "Do you know that the men are meeting with Benjamin tonight?" Reuel tried to sound matter-of-fact, because he did not want his father to notice his eagerness.

"Yes, Reuel, I just met David's father as I was coming from the sheep-fold and he told me. I think we should go over."

When they had eaten, father and son went next door. As Benjamin began to speak, Reuel looked out of the corner of his eye to see if he could tell what Hadad was thinking. But soon the boy became so absorbed that he forgot to watch.

"A few evenings ago," Benjamin said, "I told you about Jesus' decision to visit Jerusalem at the time of the Passover. Since many people would be in the city, he wanted to preach about the coming kingdom and the new way. Jesus believed with all his heart that he must be there, no matter what the scribes and chief priests might do to stop his teaching—even if they killed him.

"More than once we tried to persuade him to remain outside the city. Peter was against Jesus' plan and told him so. But Jesus became angry and said, 'You are getting in the way of what I must do. When you speak in this way, you forget that I have work to do for God.' Later Jesus talked quietly with us, explaining what he meant. 'If any man would be my follower, he must say "no" to all he wants for himself. He must take up his burden and follow me. Whoever tries to protect his life will lose it and whoever loses his life for my sake will find it.'

"At long last, Jesus and his disciples and other followers came close to the city. In fact, we were only a few miles from here, over near Bethphage, when Peter called me aside and gave me the task of finding a place for Jesus to stay for the next few nights. I went ahead into the city so that I might begin to look for lodgings.

"In Jerusalem I went directly to the pottery shop of my friend, Nahum, and told him the purpose of my errand. He was surprised that anyone would be looking for lodging in the city unless he had the money to stay in an expensive inn. He suggested that I take Jesus out here to Bethany to spend the nights during the Passover celebration.

"Nahum had learned a little of what Jesus had been doing and of what people were saying about him, so I told him that Jesus planned to enter the city in the morning. Nahum surprised me by asking, 'Is Jesus coming to the city as a king, like David?' I hadn't thought of Jesus' entry into Jerusalem this way, but the idea interested me. Would Jesus be proclaimed king as he entered the city? Would he say he was the messiah?

"The next morning Nahum and I went out to the city gate where the road from Bethphage came in. I recognized a few men who had been with Jesus in Galilee. They were standing around, as we were, waiting to see what would happen.

"After a while, we heard a few shouts outside the gate, and I saw Andrew and Thaddaeus and others of the disciples leading a small procession. In the center, sitting on a colt, was Jesus. Soon the people began to cheer. Some of them took off their cloaks and put them on the road. Others pulled leafy branches off the trees and waved a welcome. As Jesus approached, the cries increased. Those who were with Jesus and some who stood by the roadside shouted, 'Hosanna! Blessed is he who comes in the name of the Lord! He will reign on the throne of Father David! Hosanna in the highest!'

"I joined the procession, adding my voice to the chorus of 'Hosanna.' In a few moments the shouting died down, and we continued the walk toward the temple.

"Later on, some of us talked about the meaning of what had happened. We agreed that Jesus did not look like a king. He sat quietly on the colt, scarcely raising his hand to wave an answer to the people when they cheered. Yet we kept thinking of the words from the Scriptures,

> Lo, your king comes to you;
> triumphant and victorious is he,
> humble and riding on an ass.

"Nahum joined the group of followers and invited us to stay in his shop until evening, if we wished. But Jesus insisted that we go to the temple. Later we came out to this village."

One of the men in the group listening to Benjamin said, "You amaze us! We did not know that Jesus came here. Where did he stay?"

"Jesus stayed in the house of Simon and so did a few disciples. Some of the others stayed with me and still others in the house of Jesse."

Reuel whispered to his father, "That's David's grandfather. It must have been then that Jesus healed Jesse's leg." Hadad nodded his head but said nothing. He wanted to hear what else his brother had to say.

But Benjamin was only finishing his story. "There is much to tell you about all that happened in Jerusalem during the days that followed. Return in four days, and I will be here to talk with you."

Mark 8 : 31–35 ; Mark 11 : 1–10 ; Zechariah 9 : 9

CHAPTER 18

Stories of the Last Week in Jerusalem

REUEL wanted very much to know what his father thought about Benjamin's teachings, but there was no good chance to find out. Every time he was about to ask he changed his mind. No moment seemed to be right.

But Reuel and his father did talk of other things, even more than usual. Reuel told his father about the game on the hillside and about how he and Laban had become better friends than before. Reuel wasn't sure how his father would feel about his friendship with a boy who had cheated. But Hadad's response to the story was a smile and the comment, "I'm glad my son is growing to be a man—a man of righteousness, who knows and follows the law, and also a man of forgiveness and mercy."

Reuel's face lit up with pride at this. But he also wondered. He had never heard his father speak of forgiveness and mercy in just this way before. These words sounded more like Benjamin than like his father!

On another day that same week Reuel and his father talked together, this time about the words from the Scriptures that his father had read to the family—words from the prophet Jeremiah:

> Behold, the days are coming, says the LORD, when I will raise up for David a righteous Branch, and he shall reign as king and deal wisely, and shall execute justice and righteousness in the land. In his days Judah will be saved, and Israel will dwell securely.

When the reading was finished, Reuel asked a question. "Father, Benjamin speaks of the promised one too. He says that Jesus is the messiah. How will we know?"

Hadad did not answer immediately. Finally he said, "My son, I, too, am puzzled. Sometimes I find myself almost believing Benjamin when he says that Jesus is the promised one, that he is the Christ of God. But then I think of what the Scriptures say, and I am no longer certain. We will have to keep listening to Benjamin. Perhaps we will come to know what to believe."

Hadad's words did not really answer Reuel's question about the messiah, but they answered the question that had been bothering him all week. His father *was* going to keep on listening to Benjamin's stories!

The next evening Reuel and his father joined the group of men who gathered in Benjamin's dooryard. Benjamin's story went right on from where he had left off the time before.

"Tonight I will tell more of the events of the last week of Jesus' life," he began. "I saw some of what happened with my own eyes, and the rest I have heard from the twelve.

"Jesus continued to ride the colt almost to the temple area. Some of the people crowding the roads hailed him. When he came to the temple, Jesus alighted from the colt and entered the enclosure with all of us following him. He went first through the outer court where the gentiles were permitted to come. Jesus walked with a firm, determined step, as if he had long waited and planned for this day. He led us around the porches and then entered the inner courts, going as far as any but the priests could go. Wherever he walked, a crowd followed him and waited to see what he would do. But the hour was late, and soon he turned to Peter and asked him to lead the way to their lodgings.

"The next morning we returned to Jerusalem, and Jesus went directly to the temple. In the courts he saw those who sold the animals that were used for sacrifices on the temple altar. With the Passover so near, the crowd was large and business was profitable. The bleating of the animals and the shouting of the people made a great noise. As we approached the inner courts, we saw the tables of the men who changed the coins of the worshipers into the pieces of money which were required for temple taxes. People were carrying animals through the courts from one side to the other, getting in the way of worshipers and making a terrible racket. As one of the disciples said, it seemed more like a bazaar than a place of worship.

"We noticed that Jesus was becoming more and more angry at what he saw. Suddenly he could stand the sight and sound no longer. He turned to the crowd and said in a loud voice, 'What is going on here is wrong.' Then he quickly walked around the temple, overturning tables and driving out the money-changers. In the midst of the chaos Jesus stopped and said to the crowd, 'It is written in the Scriptures, "My house shall be called a house of prayer for all people." You have made it a place of cheating and making money.'

"The news of what Jesus was doing reached the chief priests and the scribes. Some of them came to the scene and stood at the edge of the crowd, talking among themselves. Many people cheered what Jesus had done, so perhaps the authorities were afraid of Jesus' power. In any case, they did not arrest him or make any trouble.

"When evening approached, we left the city and returned to Bethany. As the days went by, Jesus visited the temple several times, speaking to all who would listen to him. The religious leaders were always there watching him.

"When the day before the Passover dawned, Jesus was here in Bethany. He asked two of the disciples to go into the city to find a room where the twelve might be together for a meal. I suggested that they go to Nahum's house, where we had stayed briefly when we first reached Jerusalem. I went along to help them find the place.

"After reaching Jerusalem we went to Nahum and asked him where Jesus and his disciples could eat a meal together—a special meal in preparation for the Passover. He took us to a friend who showed us a large room on the upper floor of his house. The two disciples remained to prepare the meal, and I hurried out to Bethany to meet Jesus.

"On many other evenings, I had joined the disciples as they sat down with Jesus at supper, but on this night Jesus was alone with the twelve. I have learned what took place in the upper room from Andrew and others who were there. They told me that when Jesus ate the last supper with them, he said, 'Believe me, one who is eating here will betray me and will help my enemies to arrest me.' Each of the twelve was shocked at this and asked, 'Am I the one?' And Jesus replied, 'It is one of you, one who is eating here at this table. The time is coming when I must die. But great will be the sorrow of the one who betrays me.'

"The disciples told me also that while they were eating, Jesus took a loaf of unleavened bread and thanked God for it. Then he broke it apart and gave it to the twelve, saying as he did so, 'Take this; it is my body.' Then he took a cup of wine from the table, offered thanks to God, and gave the wine to them. They passed the cup around for each one to drink from it. Jesus said, 'This is my blood which is poured out for many in the new promise of God to his people.'

"The disciples said that after this they sang a hymn and then went out to the Mount of Olives."

Reuel had been listening to his uncle intently. He had learned months ago that Jesus had been killed, but he knew nothing of what had happened before his death. When the men had gone, Reuel asked his uncle, "Did Jesus die right after this supper?" Benjamin replied, "On the next day, Reuel. But a great deal took place before his death. I will tell about it when we next meet."

Hadad thanked Benjamin and then put his arm around his son's shoulders as they turned and walked toward their house.

Jeremiah 23:5–6; Mark 11:11, 15–19; Mark 14:12–26

CHAPTER 19

Jesus Is a Prisoner

A FEW evenings later Reuel and Hadad returned to Benjamin's house to hear more of his story. He began immediately, right from the point where he had left off the last time.

"As Jesus and the twelve disciples came down from the room where they had been eating together, eight or ten of us joined them. We had been waiting with Nahum, talking about the strange and wonderful life of our master. I noticed that Jesus and the twelve walked with a measured step that suggested a serious intention. They walked with their eyes looking downward, as if they did not notice us. Naturally, we wondered what had happened while they ate together in the upper room.

"At the outskirts of the city, just as we passed through the gate, Jesus stopped and waited for the disciples to gather around him. As we reached the cluster of people, we heard Jesus say, 'Because of what is likely to happen tonight, you will be confused and will leave me. You will be like sheep that scatter when the shepherd is hurt.'

"I could not believe this. No one had ever run away from Jesus, even when the opposition was strong. Peter gave voice to what many of us were thinking. He stepped forward and with trembling voice said, 'All the others may run away, but I will stay with you, even if I have to die.' But Jesus shook his head and said sadly, 'Peter, even you will leave me this very night. And before the rooster crows at the rising sun, you will say that you do not know me.'

"We kept walking in the direction of our village. But when we came to the place called Gethsemane, Jesus asked us to sit down and wait while he prayed. He asked Peter, James, and John to go with him. We could see that Jesus was deeply troubled. He needed all the support his friends could give.

"Of course, I did not hear what happened after the four of them left us. But some weeks later Peter and the others told us how they had failed Jesus when he needed them most. They told how Jesus asked his friends to keep watch while he prayed; then he went a little distance from them and knelt on the ground. Peter said that Jesus' prayer was like this: 'Father, all things are possible to you; may this trouble be taken away from me. But I will do what I must; I shall do whatever is your will.'

"A little later Peter, who had dozed, woke up to hear Jesus saying, 'Peter, are you sleeping too? Couldn't you stay awake for a little while? Be careful what you do. You have been eager to stay with me, but now it seems that you are weak.' Jesus went off and prayed again, and once again he had to wake up the disciples. A third time, Jesus awakened the disciples, saying, 'Are you still sleeping? The hour is at hand. Let us be going. The one who has betrayed me will be coming soon.'

"The rest of us who had remained behind when Jesus went off to pray huddled around a small fire, trying to keep the cold of the night away. All of a sudden, shouts and angry voices broke the nighttime silence.

We looked up to see torches moving up the hill, with the dark forms of the people who carried them barely visible in the distance. Jesus must have heard the commotion, too, for he came toward us, accompanied by Peter, James, and John. We could not clearly see the men who were coming for Jesus. Some looked like temple police, some like priests, and others like a gang that might have been gathered from anywhere. Then one familiar face emerged from the group—Judas, one of the disciples. He ran up to Jesus and greeted him with a kiss, saying, 'This is the man.' The temple guards seized Jesus. For a moment there was great confusion, and we could not tell what was happening, except that Jesus was standing there in the grip of the police.

When the noise and confusion subsided a little, Jesus turned to the religious leaders who seemed to be in charge and said, 'Have you followed me out here to take me as if I were a robber who was running away? Do you think you need swords and clubs? For the last week I have been in the temple teaching, and you did not take me prisoner. But let it be as it must be. I will go with you.' "

As soon as Benjamin finished speaking one of his listeners asked, "Did you follow the crowd to see what would happen?"

Benjamin answered, "No. Terrible as it is to admit it, all of us except Peter were afraid and ran away. We didn't even try to stay with Jesus. I guess we thought the temple police might take us prisoner too. Some of the men went into the city to stay with Nahum and other friends. Others came out here and to Bethphage to hide. As some of you may remember, I came home to stay for a few days."

Hadad spoke up, "Yes, I remember that you came back here. But you didn't explain to us why you had come. Tell us, Benjamin, was Jesus put to death right away by the mob?"

Before Benjamin could answer, another man asked, "Did Peter stay with Jesus to the very end?"

Benjamin replied, "The answer to both questions is no. But I will save the story of Jesus' trial and death for next time."

No words were spoken between Reuel and his father as they walked the few paces from Benjamin's home to their own, for they were both deep in thought. Reuel could not get his mind off the way in which all Jesus' followers deserted him—even Benjamin whom Reuel thought never failed in courage and in faithfulness to his friends. Reuel was almost angry as he thought about how alone Jesus had been. His followers should not have deserted him when he needed them. They should have known the right thing to do, and they should have done it as faithful disciples.

As this thought went through Reuel's mind another came like a flash—the thought of himself and Jonathan throwing pebbles at the camels. He had known that wasn't right, and yet he had thrown the pebbles anyway. All Reuel's great disappointment in himself came back, and suddenly he felt very close to Jesus' disciples.

Mark 14:27–50

CHAPTER 20

A Gathering at Jericho; a Cross at Golgotha

As the sun set, marking the end of the Sabbath, Reuel stood in front of his house looking down the road for his uncle who had been visiting in Jericho for several days. When it was so dark that Reuel could hardly see beyond the tree that hung over the road in front of his house, he caught sight of Benjamin and ran out to meet him. Hadad also saw Benjamin coming and went out to the road to invite him in for a late supper.

Hadad and his brother talked together while Benjamin ate. They spoke of the dry weather and of Benjamin's visit to Jericho. Then Benjamin said, "Tomorrow, in Jericho, there is to be a meeting of some of us who believe that Jesus is Lord. Will you come with me?"

Reuel burst out saying, "Yes, yes!" Hadad frowned at his son, but he did not seem to be angry. He turned to his brother and said, "Yes, we will go—all three of us. I can arrange for someone to care for the sheep in my place."

Early the next morning Reuel, his mother, his father, and his uncle left Bethany and walked to Jericho. Near the city, they crossed a small plain and came to a grove of trees beside a stream. A number of people were there before them.

"What will the service in Jericho be like?" Reuel asked his uncle.

"Some of it will make you think of the synagogue," Benjamin replied.

Reuel looked at the people. Then he turned to his father and said, "These people look like our neighbors. You can't tell them from those who come to our synagogue."

Hadad nodded his head.

At the beginning of the service several men offered prayers. Then another man stood and repeated words from the book of Isaiah, the prophet. So far, Reuel was reminded of the synagogue. The only thing that was different was that the name of Jesus had been mentioned in the prayers.

After the reading, Benjamin stood up and began telling the people about Jesus. After another prayer, everyone stood and said, "The goodness of the Lord Jesus be with us all. Amen."

Of course, Reuel and his father and mother did not say the words with the others. But afterwards they talked with some of the worshipers Benjamin introduced to them.

Hadad led his family back across the plain to the Jericho road, leaving his brother to join in "the breaking of bread." Benjamin would return to Bethany later in the day, and in the evening would meet with the men of Bethany again.

That evening Benjamin began by telling how he had first heard the news of Jesus' death.

"I reached Bethany an hour or two before sunrise on the morning after Jesus was taken prisoner. I stayed in my house almost all day. Perhaps I was afraid that someone would come for me, but I think I was more disappointed than afraid. There was no hope ahead; only defeat.

"When it was nearly dark, I walked out behind the village to the Jerusalem road. While I sat down on a boulder resting, a group of five Roman soldiers came along. I could not understand all that they were saying, but I did hear 'Jesus . . . cross . . . dead.' There was no question. All was finished. So I returned to my house.

"Now let me tell you about Jesus' trial before the Jewish leaders and then before Pilate. This part of the story I got from the disciples and others. Only Peter was near Jesus that night. He followed the mob right to the high priest's house. There the guards took Jesus to be questioned by many of the chief priests, elders, and scribes.

"The whole council of religious leaders had just one intention—to put Jesus to death. Many witnesses told of what they had heard Jesus say and seen him do. The stories the witnesses told did not agree with one another. Finally, the high priest stood up and put a question directly to Jesus. 'What have you to say about the words that have been spoken against you?' Jesus did not answer. Then the high priest asked another question: 'Are you the messiah?' Jesus answered, 'I am.'

"There was a great commotion in the council. The priests were more angry than ever. The high priest tore his mantle to show how shocked he was at Jesus. Then he said to the others, 'There is no need for more talk. The prisoner speaks against God. What will you do with him?'

"Every one of the religious leaders agreed that Jesus deserved death, but they did not have power to give a death sentence. Only the Roman governor could do that.

"Peter was in the courtyard of the high priest's house while all this was taking place inside. As he warmed himself by a fire, a maid servant came up to him and asked if he were one of the followers of Jesus of Nazareth. Peter quickly said, 'No.' Again she accused him, this time in front of the crowd. Again Peter denied that he knew Jesus. Then a man standing nearby also accused Peter of being one of Jesus' followers. Peter answered angrily, 'I do not know this man of whom you speak.' Just then he heard a rooster and remembered that Jesus had said, 'Before the rooster crows, you will deny me.' Peter put his head in his hands and wept.

"As soon as daylight came, the council met again and agreed to take Jesus before Pilate, the Roman governor. Pilate had not even finished his breakfast when the guards brought Jesus to him. After hearing the priests' charges against Jesus, Pilate turned to the prisoner and asked, 'Are you really the King of the Jews?' Jesus answered only, 'You have said so.'

"It was Pilate's custom to release one prisoner each year at the feast—anyone for whom the people asked. Turning to the crowd that had gathered, Pilate asked, 'Will you have me release Barabbas the murderer or Jesus, the King of the Jews?' The crowd roared, 'Barabbas.' Then Pilate asked them what they wanted him to do with Jesus. They shouted back, 'Crucify him!'

Pilate took the crowd's advice and sentenced Jesus to death on a cross. As the soldiers led the prisoner away, they made fun of him, shouting, 'Hail, King of the Jews!'

"After more of this mockery, the soldiers took Jesus outside the city to Golgotha, the place where criminals are executed. On the road they stopped Simon, from Cyrene in Africa, who was coming in from the fields, and made him carry the cross for Jesus. Two robbers were also crucified, one on each side of the Master. A sign was placed on Jesus' cross that read, 'The King of the Jews.' Nearby some of the religious leaders gathered together. As if to make fun of Jesus they cried, 'He saved others but he cannot save himself.'

"About six hours after his crucifixion, Jesus died. A centurion in charge of the soldiers said, 'Certainly this man was a son of God.' "

Benjamin stopped as if this were the end of his story for tonight. No one spoke for some time. Finally, Hadad asked, "And this was not the end, Benjamin? You believe that Jesus lives?"

"We all do, Hadad," Benjamin answered. "We serve a living Lord."

"That was what he told me many weeks ago, that Jesus came to his disciples after he had been crucified," Reuel whispered to his father. "I did not believe it then, but now I don't know."

Hadad shook his head and replied, "I don't know either, my son. It is so strange."

Mark 14: 53—15: 39

CHAPTER 21

Jesus Is Lord

WHEN Reuel woke up his first thought was that tomorrow he would be twelve years old, and he would become a shepherd like his father.

For the last few days he had thought of only two things. He had thought of Benjamin's stories about Jesus, which seemed to be more real than ever before. But just about as often Reuel had remembered that he was almost twelve years old. He pictured in his mind what it would be like to be a shepherd and work with his father each day.

As Reuel left the house and walked toward the synagogue, he saw David waiting for him a little way ahead. "The great Peter is coming to Bethany!" David shouted to him as soon as he was within hearing range.

Reuel caught his friend's excitement and asked, "Will it be soon?"

"Yes! This very afternoon he is coming!" David replied. "My father came back from Jerusalem late last night with the news. He is going to tell Benjamin and the others right away this morning. We're all to meet him on the hillside. Do you think you can come?"

"I'll come!" Reuel answered without any hesitation.

All morning Reuel thought about going to hear Peter. He wondered if his father would get the news in time.

When school was out he hurried home, hoping that his father would be there. As he ran into the yard, he was relieved to see Benjamin and Hadad talking together.

Reuel knew he should not interrupt their conversation, so he just listened. Evidently his father had asked about Peter because Benjamin was saying, "I told you that he denied that he was one of Jesus' followers at the time of the trial. But that is all past. For a long time he has been going out from Jerusalem to preach the good news about Jesus."

"But why should Peter do this?" Hadad asked. "Why do *you* spend your time telling the story of Jesus?"

Benjamin replied, "Because we must. It's hard to explain why. Peter tells us that after the crucifixion, when the disciples returned to their homes in Galilee, they knew Jesus was with them there, and they knew he was saying something like this: 'The power of God has been given to me. Go wherever you can, both near and far, and ask others to be disciples. Baptize them. Teach them to live by what I have taught you. And remember this when you need strength—I am with you always, even to the end of the world.'

"This is what Peter has been doing. And the rest of us have tried to do what we can. Now Peter is coming to Bethany, and we will hear him preach. I hope you will come, Hadad."

Then Benjamin left to tell the news to others in the village. Reuel turned to his father and looked at him inquiringly.

"Yes," his father said, "we will go—and Mother too. I hope this is the right thing to do," he added.

When sunset was only an hour away, Reuel's family joined the group of people on their way out to a hillside just above Bethany. Reuel saw many of his friends with their families, but some were missing—Laban and, of course, the rabbi. When they got to the hillside everyone sat down on the ground and waited. Reuel stretched to try to see Benjamin because he thought that Peter might be with him. "I see him," Reuel said to his mother. "He must be that big man who is sitting between Benjamin and David's father."

Soon Peter stood up and began to speak: "Fellow Jews, do not expect me to do anything that is amazing. All that I am able to say and do is by the goodness of God. This God of our fathers, the one whom Abraham and Isaac and Jacob worshiped, has made his servant Jesus glorious to us. Our religious leaders arrested Jesus and brought him to Pilate for trial. Pilate condemned him to death. The people—people like you—refused to accept this holy and righteous servant of God and asked for a murderer to be released instead of Jesus. The people killed the one who came to bring them life. But God has raised him up! He lives!

"Now, brothers, I know the people did not realize what they were doing when they crucified Jesus. Even the religious authorities did not know whom they were condemning to death. But now you must know that God has made Jesus Lord and Christ!"

Reuel was listening so intently that he jumped when one of the men in the crowd called out to Peter, "What shall we do now?"

"Repent and turn to God, that your sins may be wiped out. A new, fresh power will come to you, for the presence of the Lord Jesus Christ is among you. Truly, God will help you find your deliverance in Jesus.

"Think on this. Remember that Moses said, 'The Lord God will send a prophet from among you, and you shall listen to this prophet. If you do not listen, you will be lost.' And Moses was not the only one who spoke this message in times past. All the prophets have made the same promise to our people.

"You are not strangers to God. You are the sons of the prophets and have inherited the promise which God gave to your fathers—'In your children shall all the families of the earth be blessed.'

"God, who raised his servant Jesus from the dead, offers him to you, so that you may be blessed, all of you, as you turn from wickedness. This Jesus is your Lord!"

Peter said much more, and Reuel tried to understand everything. It was dark by the time Peter stopped and stood silent in front of the crowd. No one said a word. After a moment Peter walked a short distance away, and some of the men went over to talk with him. Hadad and Benjamin were among them. Since it was very late Reuel had to go back home with his mother.

As much as he could remember of Peter's sermon kept going around in Reuel's mind as he lay on his mat unable to sleep. The name of Jesus kept coming to him again and again. He thought, "I know that Jesus is the promised one! I know it!"

Reuel was still awake when his father came in. He listened carefully as Hadad spoke quietly to his wife. "Benjamin and Peter are right!" he said. "I believe! I believe that Jesus is Lord!"

Reuel sat up. "I believe, too," he said. "I believe that Jesus is Lord! Tomorrow, first thing, on my birthday, I'm going to Benjamin to tell him I believe!"

Matthew 28:19–20; Acts 3:13–26

Pronouncing Names of People and Places

Barabbas	bar-ab'bas
Bethphage	beth'fa-gee
Caesarea Philippi	ses'a-ree'a fil-lip'pie
Cleopas	klee'o-pus
Damascus	da-mas'kus
Elijah	ee-lie'ja
Gethsemane	geth-sem'a-nee
Golgotha	gol'go-tha
Hadad	hay'dad
Isaiah	eye-zay'a
Laban	lay'ban
Levite	lee'vite
Messiah	me-sigh'a
Nahum	nay'hum
Reuel	roo'el
Thaddaeus	tha-dee'us
Zacchaeus	za-kee'us
Zebedee	zeb'e-dee